TAKING CONTROL OF YOUR CAREER AND YOUR FUTURE:

FOR NURSES, BY NURSES

Gail J. Donner, RN, PhD
Mary M. Wheeler, RN, MEd

Editors

**Taking Control of Your Career and Your Future:
For Nurses, By Nurses**

ISBN: 1-55119-021-4

Published by the Canadian Nurses Association, 1998.

Edited by
Gail J. Donner, RN, PhD
Mary M. Wheeler, RN, MEd

Acknowledgements

Any successful endeavour is rarely accomplished alone. So it also is with this book. This project is the result of the contributions and determination of a number of people. Without them, our vision for this book would never have been realized.

Thanks to chapter authors Linda, Anne, Lisa, Lorna, Janice, Betty, Dorothy, and Eleanor for their confidence in us, for their enthusiasm for this project, and for their willingness to share their knowledge and experience.

Barbara Bauer acted as developmental and copy editor, as guide and coach. Her tireless effort and ongoing commitment to the development of this book helped make it come alive; she was able to help us translate what we wanted to say into something that others would understand – and all with patience, good humour, and an unrivalled commitment to creating an excellent product. Marion DeLand, Claire Mallette, Mary McAllister, Alice Milne, and Kim Salonen reviewed sections of the manuscript and provided us with honest and useful feedback. Jamie Brown gave us wise counsel; and Heather George provided excellent administrative and secretarial support. We also want to thank the Canadian Nurses Association (CNA), who identified the need Canadian nurses had expressed for help with career development and who agreed to publish this book. In particular, Norah Brochu, Ondina Love and Hugh Malcolm at CNA deserve special mention.

Support, encouragement, and being more than you ever thought you could be is what this book is really about. For that we need to thank our families, the Wheeler nieces and nephews who stuffed packages, all the brothers, sisters, and in-laws who encouraged us, Elizabeth and Simon, who always provide perspective, but especially Arthur and Loretto, who have been with us every step of our career journeys and who provide us with the love and support that help us see what is possible and then go for it!

Dedication

This book is dedicated to the more than 3,000 nurses we have met over the past 6 years through our work in career planning and development. They should be credited with challenging us to put our thoughts and experiences in writing so that we could share our ideas with nurses everywhere. They understood and shared our passion and commitment to nursing and to nurses, and for that we are grateful.

Table of Contents

UNIT I

The Career Planning Process

CHAPTER ONE
Taking Control of Your Future: The Time is Now

CHAPTER TWO
Beginning the Process: Scanning Your Environment

CHAPTER THREE
Completing Your Self-Assessment and Reality Check

CHAPTER FOUR
Creating Your Career Vision

CHAPTER FIVE
Developing Your Strategic Career Plan

CHAPTER ONE

Taking Control of Your Future: The Time is Now

Gail J. Donner, RN, PhD

Gail Donner is currently Associate Dean, Education, and Professor at the Faculty of Nursing, University of Toronto, where she is also a Co-Investigator of the Nursing Effectiveness, Utilization, and Outcomes Research Unit. Gail's teaching and research interests are in career development, health policy, the role of nurse managers, and bioethics education. Gail is also a Partner in Donner & Wheeler and Associates, a consulting firm specializing in career planning and development within the health and social service sectors.

Nursing in the last half of the 20th century has been marked by tremendous change. It has been transformed from an occupation whose members struggled within a social context that devalued nurses' work as "women's work" to a profession comprised of autonomous, well educated, career-oriented knowledge workers. These changes have created new roles, new work settings and new colleagues for nurses. Now we can work in a variety of settings – in institutions, in communities, and in independent businesses. We work alone, with other nurses, or in multidisciplinary teams in our roles as clinicians, educators, researchers, consultants, or managers. Moreover, nurses are presidents and chief executive officers (CEOs) of health care agencies, policy analysts, and politicians. All of these roles use the skills, knowledge, and spirit that nursing education and experience provide. These extraordinary changes have brought significant challenge along with terrific opportunity. As we have moved from thinking of and living with nursing as a job to considering nursing as a career, we have taken more charge of the profession and begun to look at how to create futures for nurses as individuals and for the profession as a whole. This perceptual shift from viewing nursing as an episodic series of jobs to seeing it as a lifelong career has undoubtedly been the most significant change in nursing since Florence Nightingale professionalized nursing in the late 19th century.

These developments in nursing have coincided with equally dramatic changes taking place in the health care systems and in the economies of most developed countries. Cycles of boom and bust as well as of high unemployment and shortages of workers have been common, and change has been the norm. The changes in nursing and in how it is perceived by nurses and by society, along with the changes in the health care system, together have created an environment in which individuals must become career resilient and self-directed, where they must take control of their careers and futures.

Regardless of whether change is planned or unplanned, or initiated by the employee or the employer, many factors influence a nurse's ability to thrive on the opportunities created and grow with change rather than merely react against it. Most nurses know they need to take control of their working lives and futures to make the most of change, but they often do not know where or how to begin. Continuous career planning is a strategy that can offer nurses the means to respond to both short- and long-term changes in their profession and in the health care system. Career planning is "a continuous process of self-assessment and goal setting" (Kleinknecht & Hefferin, 1982, p.31). The process of planning and developing your career is an integral part of your ongoing professional development. Furthermore, the skills required to engage in career planning are those same skills nurses already use in their daily practice as part of problem solving and the nursing process. Just as you develop care plans with and for your patients, so too must you learn to design career plans for yourself. The skills you rely on are the same, but the focus or target is different.

For the past several years the editors of this book have been consulting with nurses and employers of nurses and have conducted career planning and development workshops with over 3,000 nurses. These workshops were directed towards helping nurses take charge of their careers and learn how to integrate career development into their ongoing professional and personal development. What we have learned from the many nurses who have participated in these workshops is that nurses need and want help with this important part of their development, that nurses have dreams, goals, and ideas about their futures, but that they need a process to guide them in achieving those futures. Our book, therefore, is meant to provide nurses with a model they can use to guide their career development and with practical strategies for identifying and achieving success and satisfaction as they define it.

This book will address the need to take control of your future, why career planning is an issue now, and how to make it a part of your ongoing professional development. Then the book will give you the tools to transform your understanding into reality. It is not meant to function as a quick fix or recipe book, but rather it offers an approach to living a rewarding and autonomous professional life. While it is not specifically a job search book, many of the strategies presented will be invaluable in helping you find the job you want, even in a difficult employment environment. It is written for every nurse – for those beginning a career in nursing as well as those planning their retirement; for those wanting a change within nursing and for those contemplating a move away from nursing; for those who want to continue to work in organizations and for those who want to be independent practitioners; for those who love what they do and want to continue to do it; and for those who want to move along in any direction. The book also provides a resource for those who teach, both in schools of nursing and in clinical settings, and for managers and organizations interested in supporting their staff through professional development.

THE STAGES OF A NURSING CAREER

Career planning can play a crucial role at every stage of one's career. Nurses' careers generally can be described as passing through four stages (Donner, 1992). Stage one, the entry phase, begins when newly graduated nurses select their first workplace. It is that time of one's career when nurses explore their various employment options and begin to think about areas of practice that could be both appropriate and rewarding. In the second stage, the commitment phase, nurses identify their likes and dislikes in terms of clinical areas, geography, worklife, etc. At this point, anywhere from 2 to 5 years following graduation, nurses evaluate their career goals, seek mentors, consider continuing their education, and generally seek to find the right "fit" between themselves and their work settings. This is the time when nurses' focus on job shifts to a focus on career and long-term commit-ment. In the third stage, the consolidation phase, nurses become comfortable with their chosen career path and with their relationship between the personal and the professional. This stage is notable for nurses' dedication to career, commitment to continuous learning, and focus on making a contribution to health care and to society. It is when the nurse begins to mentor others and to assume a leadership role in professional and community organizations. In the fourth or withdrawal stage, nurses prepare for retirement and begin to think about what comes after nursing.

As you move through your career, your skills develop, your needs change, and your goals and plans evolve. Career planning is thus both important and useful at every stage of your career. It is a dynamic process that changes and adapts to changes in you and in the world in which you live and work. The career planning and development model that follows will provide you with a framework from which to grow and develop as a professional and to build your career in a comprehensive way.

THE CAREER PLANNING AND DEVELOPMENT MODEL

Career development is a process. Iterative rather than linear, it requires individuals to understand the environment in which they live and work, assess their own strengths and limitations and validate that assessment, articulate their personal career vision, and develop a plan for the future that is realistic for them. Simply put, it is a focused professional development strategy that helps nurses take greater responsibility for themselves and their careers and prepare for ever changing health care systems and workplace environments. The four phases of the process are (a) scanning your environment, (b) completing your self-assessment and reality check, (c) creating your career vision, and (d) developing your strategic career plan.

Scanning Your Environment

Scanning your environment can be described as taking stock of the world in which you live. It involves understanding the current realities in the health care system and the work environment as well as the future trends at the global, national, and local levels both within and outside of health care and the nursing profession. Through the scanning process you become better informed, learn to see the world through differing perspectives, and are able to identify career opportunities, both current and future. Scanning is a continuous activity, which together with self-assessment forms the foundation of the career planning process. We observe, learn about, and assess the world around us through reading, talking with others, and continuing our education, and through exposing ourselves not only to information and ideas from and about nursing and health care, but from other disciplines and ideologies as well. It is from this solid understanding of our environment that we go on to complete a self-assessment.

Completing Your Self-Assessment and Reality Check

Just as you would not consider developing a patient care plan without a thorough patient assessment, so it is with career planning. A thorough self-assessment is the key to exploring new and previously unconsidered opportunities. It enables you to identify your values, experiences, knowledge, strengths, and limitations and to marry those with your environmental scan to create your career vision and identify the directions to take as you plan your future. And just as we seek validation in our patient assessments, so too should we also complete a reality check of our self-assessment. A reality check is simply about seeking feedback regarding our strengths and limitations – about expanding our view of ourselves through reflecting on others' perspectives.

Creating Your Career Vision

Once you have determined a realistic and comprehensive picture of your own values, beliefs, and skills, and looked at those in the context of the real world scan you have completed, you are ready to think about your career possibilities. Where is it you see yourself going? Do you like what you are currently doing, feel it is a good fit with your personal life, and want to grow and develop within that role or have you learned that you enjoy change and variety and that it may be time to move on to other challenges? Because your vision of your potential future is grounded in your scan and self-assessment, it is focused on what is possible and realistic for you, both in the short and the longer term. Your career vision is the link between who you are and what you can become.

Developing Your Strategic Career Plan

A strategic career plan is a blueprint for action. According to Barker (1992), vision without action is only a dream; action without vision only passes the time; but vision with action can change the world. Now you are ready to specify the activities, time lines, and resources you need to help you achieve your goals and career vision. This is the part of the process where you start to put on paper the specific strategies you will use to take charge of your future. Of course, this is also where the spiral or iterative nature of the process is reinforced. Although, for example, you may have planned to do some diabetic teaching to your patient, if you enter the room and see a very anxious and distraught patient with a nearly hysterical family at the bedside, you would undoubtedly reassess your plan and adapt it to the current environment. So it is with career planning. We should be constantly scanning our environment, assessing ourselves, and re-evaluating our goals and our plans for reaching them.

HOW TO USE THIS BOOK

This book is a guide that, as with a travel guide, we should each use in the way that best suits our style. Career planning is a serious process that takes time and perseverance. If you want to learn to be a lifelong career planner, then you will need to devote some time to the phases of the process that are outlined in Chapters Two, Three, Four, and Five of Unit I. Their authors will provide you with both an understanding of the phases of the process and with some specific strategies and questions to guide you in using the process to develop a comprehensive strategic career plan.

Unit I also provides you with the details of the career planning model. Linda McGillis Hall has scanned the current environment to help you understand the world of health and health care and provide you with a guide for your own scanning. Gail Donner has asked the questions you need to consider in order to assess who you are and what you have to offer. Mary Wheeler has shown you how to match your environmental scan with your self-assessment to create your personal career vision and determine your career goals. Anne Coghlan has provided you with an outline and directions to enable you to design your own strategic career plan to achieve those goals.

In Unit II you will learn how to take your strategic career plan and make it work for you. In Chapter Six, Lisa Pearlman will help you apply what you learned from completing your self-assessment so that you can present yourself in the best possible light. Her assistance with constructing résumés and covering letters, along with other self-marketing strategies, will help ensure that you achieve your career vision. Then Lorna Hegarty and Mary Wheeler will provide timely and focused direction on the interviewing process and how to make sure that it works for you. Together Lisa, Lorna, and Mary will help you identify transferable skills, target your activities to the potential employer, and generally integrate what you have learned from the career planning process into your job search.

The career continuum is the focus of Unit III. If you are a student, Janice Waddell has some tips for you! In Chapter Eight, she will help beginners in nursing learn how to adapt the career planning process to their particular needs. Janice will show how students can use their student clinical experiences along with their non-nursing experiences and expertise to help achieve their career goals. She has also provided samples of student résumés.

One of the benefits that the ever changing health care environment has yielded is the opportunity for nurses to pursue independent practice or entrepreneurship. Betty Gourlay, an independent practitioner, provides the answers to some of the questions asked by many nurses considering this option: What is independent practice? How do I know if it's for me? How do I get started? And how do I maintain my career as an entrepreneur? The strategies Betty discusses are also helpful for working inside organizations where intrapreneurship is promoted and valued.

The withdrawal stage of a nursing career requires thoughtful planning too. In Chapter Ten Dorothy Wylie, who had a long, successful and well respected career in nursing, has provided guidance related to the last phase of a career – planning for retirement. Use the advice she has offered about some of the legal, financial, and social issues that you must attend to if you want to ensure a happy and productive retirement from an equally happy and productive career.

Thus far, we have considered the nurse as an individual engaged in his or her own career planning. But, clearly, there is a role for employers, professional organizations, unions, and educators in the career planning process. The last unit of the book is devoted to what can happen beyond the individual level. Investing in employees has long been considered a wise business strategy. Those who are happy with their careers and their workplaces are productive and committed employees. If you are involved in organizational strategic planning in any way, either as a manager or a staff nurse, you will find helpful advice in Eleanor Ross's and Mary Wheeler's discussion about how employers can provide career development consultation and support for their employees. They both examine the principles underpinning the process and provide a real life example of how one organization made career development of its employees a priority in the best interests of the workplace as well as the workers.

Having now engaged in the career planning process and having identified the place you fit in the future, you may be interested in knowing more about other career planning resources. In Chapter Twelve Gail Donner and Mary Wheeler discuss the many partners that must be involved in career development to ensure that both your individual goals and nursing's collective vision are realized.

TAKING CONTROL

Attending to your professional development is a time intensive process that requires reflection as well as planning. The career planning process presented in this book gives you a way of relating your ideas and vision with the practical realities of your life in order to achieve useful and realizable outcomes. It represents an approach whereby you can get the most out of yourself and your career while you give the most to your clients. The career planning process is really about the development of a life skill, one that you can apply not only in your workplace, but in your personal life as well. The process described in this book is not magical, nor is it relevant only for nurses. Although it can be used as a personal guide, it can also be shared with family and friends. A career needs attention and nurturing. This book is intended to provide you with the skills you need in order to care for yourself and your career. Use it in good health!

REFERENCES

Barker, J. (1992). *Paradigms: The business of discovering the future.* New York: Harper Collins.

Donner, G. J. (1992). Career development and mobility issues. In A. Baumgart & J. Larsen (Eds.), *Canadian nursing faces the future* (2nd ed., pp. 345-363). St. Louis, MO: Mosby Year Book.

Kleinknecht, M. K., & Hefferin, E. A. (1982). Assisting nurses toward professional growth: A career development model. *Journal of Nursing Administration, 12*(5), 30-36.

CHAPTER TWO

Beginning the Process: Scanning Your Environment

Linda McGillis Hall, RN, MSc, PhD (Cand.)

Linda McGillis Hall is a doctoral candidate at the Faculty of Nursing, University of Toronto. There she is also currently a Lecturer and a Co-Investigator with the Nursing Effectiveness, Utilization, and Outcomes Research Unit, a joint project between the University of Toronto and McMaster University. Linda's publications are primarily in the area of nursing administration and staff mix.

When asked to think about the word "environment," you should conjure up not only a close-up picture of the setting in which health care is practised, but also a wide-angle shot of the broader area surrounding you, that is, the external conditions within which you live. For just as you would not consider providing care to clients without knowing something about their family and socio-economic circumstances as well as their health status, so too in order to understand how current trends and future developments in health care could affect your career, you must think about the broader context of your external environment as well. Scanning the environment and completing a self-assessment form the foundation of the career planning process. Scanning will provide you with the information you need to understand your current world and to identify possible opportunities and options for developing your career in the future. You must have a solid understanding of the environment before you can decide how to use your skills and experience in the most beneficial way, both for you and for society.

In this chapter you will learn about the scanning process – why it is important, what to scan, how to scan, and when to scan. The chapter will then provide you with a scan of the current environment, which begins with an outline of the shifts in health care at a broad societal level and then continues to identify the system-level changes that reflect these global shifts. The response of individual organizations to global and system changes and the challenge imposed upon them to manage within a reformed system are discussed, along with the impact of these changes on the individual and on employer-employee relations. The current and future implications of these reforms for nurses and for their career development will be considered. Finally, the stages in the environmental scanning process will be reviewed from the perspective of individual career planning and development.

THE WHY, WHAT, WHEN, AND HOW OF SCANNING YOUR ENVIRONMENT

Scanning is the easiest and most productive way to place yourself as an observer, rather than a player, in the world in which you live. You can, thereby, see beyond your immediate circumstances to grasp what is possible, to think about new things in new ways, and to open yourself to opportunities without any censoring of ideas.

When you enter a client's room, whether in a hospital or in the client's home, the first thing you do is look around to get a picture of the environment within which the client lives and within which you will have to deliver care. Scanning your own personal and professional environments, that is, in the world in which you live and work, is a similar activity you can pursue to help you to reflect upon the circumstances influencing your world so that you can decide how best to adapt to and make use of the environment – to plan your career just as you plan the client's care. If you learn as much as possible about what forces and elements you are dealing with, you can take advantage of some, compensate for missing ones, and redirect or mitigate the effects of others. Simply put, scanning the environment and then identifying your own strengths and interests (as you will learn to do in Chapter Three) will give you the information you need to make and then implement a plan to successfully develop your career.

Throughout our careers, each of us must scan, continuously, and in a variety of ways to learn about what is happening and what may be happening in the future. Sources of information include professional and popular journals, observation, print and other forms of new media, friends and colleagues, and everyday experiences. Reading, talking, and listening, skills that nurses have as part of their repertoire of behaviours, are the means we use to make sense of all of the information we collect. Scanning, therefore, becomes not a task to be completed at some regular or not so regular time, but rather an integral part of everyday professional and personal life.

Those nurses, for example, who have been following international developments in hospital restructuring have been able to anticipate the kinds of changes that Canadian hospitals may experience. They have been able to recognize that opportunities in hospitals will continue to be limited in the future, but that community opportunities may open up for them either as employees or as independent practitioners. Instead of waiting to see what might happen, they are readying themselves by thinking, learning, and planning to meet some of the challenges and the opportunities that, for instance, limited hospital beds and shortened lengths of stay may provide. Without continuous scanning, it is very difficult to use your own skills to their best advantage, very difficult to know the best direction in which to head, and even more difficult to feel in control of your own future. To help you understand what an environmental scan looks like so that you can begin to develop your own scanning skills, let us take a look at the current health care environment as an example.

An Environmental Scan

Since the environment is constantly changing, what follows is a sample scan of it done at one particular time. But you should think of your scan as a work in progress, something you continuously update and revise to reflect the changing environment. If you are thereby prepared, you should be able to identify the global, national, and local trends and issues that, at any given time, shape the environment, your practice, and your future.

Health Care Trends

Throughout the past decade, tremendous shifts in the health care environment have occurred throughout the world. Spurred by global economic and social changes, the health care system has undergone dramatic reform. These reforms include shifts in health care funding that have resulted in considerable restructuring, downsizing, and re-engineering of work processes in the practice environment.

Cutbacks to funding

In Canada, health care has undergone unprecedented changes over the past decade primarily as a consequence of the increase in health care spending that took place throughout the 1970s and 1980s. The federal and provincial governments' response to this trend was to decrease the overall funding provided for health care while increasing accountability for how these health care dollars were being spent. For the first time, in 1990, health care funding transfers from the federal budget to the provinces were frozen for a 2-year period. This event heralded the beginning of some of the most dramatic financial cutbacks in Canada's health care history. These cutbacks reflected a change in federal policy that, in turn, created pressure at the provincial level to contain health care costs. Together these influences changed the face of health care delivery in Canada.

Provincial response to these cutbacks was swift. With scant transition, the health care system, which was accustomed to having no spending limits, was forced into an era of cost containment. The "penny had dropped," and hospitals were caught in the middle. Despite a decrease in patient length of stay, hospital costs were rising. Questions began to emerge about whether variations in practice and treatment across hospital sites and geographic regions were justifiable from the perspective of patient outcomes or quality of care. Examination of physician practice patterns and utilization rates became the norm as efforts were pursued to improve the efficiency of practice while decreasing costs (Naylor, Anderson, & Goel, 1994). A perception developed that nurses, known to be a large source of labour in hospitals because of their around-the-clock work with patients, were costly rather than cost effective (McGillis Hall, 1997). As we approach the 21st century, the market for nursing services is uncertain, and many nurses in all walks of nursing life have experienced layoffs or enforced early retirement – often an entirely new experience for them.

Rise of consumer-driven models

In addition to these extensive shifts, a number of other significant changes were also beginning to influence health care delivery in Canada during this time, one of the most consequential being the move away from provider-driven models of health care delivery to consumer-driven models. As they had in the business environment, where customer satisfaction became a key issue, consumers were emerging as the dominant force in the health care provider-consumer relationship. They have become more educated about the health care choices and alternatives available to them and are demanding a health care system that is configured more towards their needs. Evidence of consumer involvement in health care includes the development of patients' rights statements, legislation relating to consumer advocacy, and a trend towards increasing the role and numbers of consumers as trustees on boards of health care agencies (Sutherland & Fulton, 1992). Mechanisms to elicit and assess patient satisfaction became common in health care organizations, and patient representative roles emerged in an effort to help identify and manage patient concerns with health care practices.

Influences of technology

As well, the tremendous technological advances in health care that have been occurring simultaneously have had a marked effect on health care, and have added to consumers' expectations of the health care system. For example, many illnesses are being treated today that at one time could not even be diagnosed. Great progress has been made in the areas of organ transplantation and microscopic surgery. Most recently, a new trend towards non-invasive treatments has emerged. As one would expect, these technological advances are expensive and have created a pyramid effect that has had a dramatic impact on overall health care costs. They have also created a paradox for health care officials who must constantly weigh the interests of the consumer against the costs of providing the care. Nursing roles have evolved as nurses have developed the technical expertise needed to manage patients following these complex procedures and treatments, both in hospitals and in the community.

Computerization has had significant effects, as well, on health care and on nursing practice. It will continue to pose a challenge for nurses as we learn to understand both the computer's potential to influence our practice and its larger role in health care delivery. This challenge represents a great opportunity for those nurses who see the computer as a friend; such nurses can act as valuable resources to others who are uncomfortable with the prospect of increasing computerization.

Health promotion

Meanwhile, health promotion has become the central focus of health policy as the overall view of health in society has evolved from one focused on illness to one interested in promoting wellness (Lalonde, 1974). Programs have been developed that are directed at teaching the public how to protect their health and maintain their well-being (Epp, 1986). The consumer, however, is being provided with double messages related to the social aspects of health care. Despite the considerable attention directed towards the idea of promoting the health of Canadian society, the medical establishment and hospitals have exerted conflicting pressures to promote the high technology curative processes of medicine (Rachlis & Kushner, 1994). Health care organizations are desperately trying to retain their status in the community, or sometimes just to remain in service. Even though early health care interventions are cheaper, simpler, and often more effective than high-technology specialist care, institutional and medical sectors of the health care system continue to be over-emphasized.

While there seems to be widespread agreement that health promotion is the essential direction in which our health care system should go, many argue that Canadian society is currently in a period of transition. Once again, a paradox is evident. The field of medicine is all about dealing with the consequences of not having had health promotion programs in place in the past. Many of the diseases that are creating large cost burdens to the health care system are those associated with chronic conditions that are preventable, such as heart disease and respiratory illnesses. With an aging population, this burden can soon be expected to grow even further. Yet despite this assertion, it is essential that health reforms continue to focus on promoting healthy behaviour to move the population away from a future of chronic illness. To support such reforms, providers must shift their thinking, and the focus of the health care delivery system must move from the hospital to the community. For example, nurses need to expand their thinking about possible career options within this reformed system by de-emphasizing traditional roles. Hospital nurses can explore ways to apply their knowledge through careers within the community that move beyond traditional "public health" or "visiting nurse" roles and focus on the specific clinical expertise they possess.

Community health

The area of community health has been slow to emerge in Canada where the focus of health care had been primarily institutional or hospital-based. Traditionally, community health settings emphasize preventive medicine and health promotion rather than the episodic, curative approaches to health care common in hospital settings. But over the past few years in Canada, a great deal of interest has been directed towards enhancing community health. Since the dramatic decrease in hospital funding that has occurred in the 1990s, the hospital sector has reacted more favourably towards the idea of outreach to the community.

As hospitals have begun to look at alternatives to cut the costs of patient care, their most prevalent response has been shortened hospital length of stay. The consequential decreased length of patient hospital stays, however, has resulted in a corresponding increase in patient need for care within the community. But it has been difficult to adapt traditional community nursing practice patterns to accommodate these changes, especially without the ability to increase nursing staff volumes. Once again, expert hospital nurses have a tremendous opportunity to develop their careers by devising responses to these challenges that would meet both the new community and the hospital sector needs. As well, the role of the primary care nurse practitioner provides nurses with the opportunity to expand their practice while working with physicians in a complementary role in the community.

Summary

What is obvious about the numerous changes to the health care system that have been described as reforms is the lack of integration between hospital and community practice. This purposeful shift of patient care underway from the hospital to the community was not foreseen or planned by hospitals. More important, corresponding funds from hospitals were not directed into the community to support and absorb these patient shifts out of hospitals. Rather, the community has been left to bear these burdens within their own set of cost containment circumstances. Therefore, one of the most significant challenges facing the health system today relates to the need to shift resources into the community to support the provision of care there. As well, further work is needed to direct the future of health human resource planning for the community. For example, although primary nurse practitioner roles have developed, legislation and secure funding must be in place to avoid a lack of consistency in practice and potential confusion for the public. Similarly, nurses undertaking independent practice in the community are faced with challenges related to how they fit into the existing systems.

Structural Reforms

The global reforms to health care that have occurred have had considerable impact on the structures for delivering care.

Regionalization

One of the first structural changes was in the pattern of health care governance with the move towards regionalization of services. At a local level this regionalization takes on a number of forms. One system for regionalization in Ontario, for example, occurs through District Health Councils (DHCs), which serve as planning and advisory bodies for different geographic areas of the province. In other provinces, for example, New Brunswick and Alberta, regional authorities have been established to plan and deliver health care to designated geographical areas. This change has led to the closure of numbers of institutions and the merger of others. In such a system, a nurse would have one employer, the regional organization, but would spend his or her time in a particular member health care agency of that regional organization.

Hospital governance

Governance is another area affected by structural reform. Hospital governance is evolving from an era where individual hospital boards had autonomy and control over the practices and processes within their hospitals. Now a variety of models reflect a mix of local interests that are balanced to meet broader health care needs and the objectives of regional service delivery networks (Baker, 1992). As a result, models are emerging that have one hospital board administering a number of institutions in the region, often with one budget and one president. This move away from autonomous single organizations towards coordinated service entities is the first step towards an integrated health care delivery system.

Integrated delivery systems

Shortell, Gillies, Anderson, Erickson, and Mitchell (1996) suggest that the major forces driving health care in the 1990s, which include technological change, the information explosion, demographic shifts, a restructured work force, and the growing demand for value, all point to the need for an integrated approach. Organized delivery systems would integrate the care of patients in communities and focus on enhancing the health status of the communities served by the system (Shortell et al., 1996). Integrated delivery systems have emerged in Canada as a way of linking the concepts behind traditional hospital health care delivery systems to the notion of community health and well-being. Dagnone (1996) defined integrated delivery networks as a network of organizations that provides or arranges to provide a coordinated continuum of services to a defined population and that assumes clinical and fiscal accountability for both the outcomes of those services and the health status of the population served. Integrated delivery systems depend on strong primary health care systems and often include rostering and capitation as methods for defining populations and determining remuneration to primary care providers. Several reports across the country have identified the need for integrated delivery systems, and some models are emerging.

   One of the key tactics directing the current restructuring process is to wean the system participants away from an independent service provider orientation by improving partnerships and strategic alliances amongst organizations. Strategic alliances can provide a number of benefits to the participants, including knowledge and skills transfer, technical assistance, experience, financing and capital contributions, access to technology, training support and education, and economies of scale

(Dagnone, 1996; Shortell et al., 1996). Collaboration and partnerships among health care providers will be required within workplaces as well as between hospitals and the community to support these health reforms to the system. Nurses have an opportunity to play a key role in these redesigned structures by taking the initiative to devise roles for themselves that would bridge the gaps between these provider groups.

Changes Within the Workplace

The structural reforms in health care that are being implemented, not only in Canada but throughout the developed world, have been accompanied by many changes at the workplace level. Structural changes resulting from re-engineering have led to changes in the roles of both management and staff in health care organizations and to changes in employer-employee relationships.

Re-engineering

In hospitals, organizational structures have become flatter and leaner through organizational change strategies such as downsizing, re-engineering, and rightsizing (Leatt, Baker, Halverson, & Aird, 1997). Hammer & Champy (1993) describe re-engineering as the radical redesign of an organization's processes, organization, and culture. Throughout the 1990s this radical redesign has been applied almost continuously to hospitals, where many of the management, supervisory, and support role layers have been eliminated. Therefore, despite the fact that hospitals remain the largest employer of nurses in Canada, fewer opportunities for career advancement exist within the hospital environment. At the same time, decreases in patient length of stay and hospital bed occupancy have resulted in layoffs at the staff level. Compounding the effects of these events, radical changes also have occurred in the position of nursing in hospital environments. These changes do not need to limit nursing opportunities, but they do mean that nurses have to broaden their definition of nursing work and nursing workplaces.

Changing role of nurse executives

Business processes have been used to redesign and flatten the structure of health care organizations. Departments have been reconfigured into patient service areas that are organized by programs or grouped by patient diagnosis. To support this orientation towards patients, existing departments are redistributed within these programs. One of the most significant shifts has been in the area of nursing where entire nursing departments have been abolished and nursing has been dispersed into the individual patient service groupings. In many cases the profession of nursing has been relabelled as a service occupation within the organizational structure. Once the nursing service has been redistributed and the nursing department dissolved, there is no longer a role for a department head of nursing. However, in most reconfigured institutions, it was still thought necessary to have some role for a nursing leader in the organizational chart, since nurses still remain the largest provider group for patient care in hospitals. What often results is the position of chief of nursing practice, which entails little if any fiscal power or authority. Some see this dissolution of nursing departments as a serious threat to the status and influence of nursing in the hospital and as the first step in the systematic weakening of nursing's role in the management of patient care in hospitals.

Changes to patient care delivery

Other changes occurring at the same time in hospitals, such as decreases in patient length of stay, have forced changes in the organization and delivery of patient care. Health care policy makers have concluded that there are too many acute care beds. But rather than closing an entire hospital, they often merge patient care units within the hospital. Consequently, managers, who now frequently oversee a number of units, are less accessible and visible on any one unit and less available to the staff reporting to them. As a result, it is often the registered nurse who experiences the burden of the organizational changes at the unit level. Staff nurses have taken on many of the unit administration responsibilities in addition to providing and coordinating the care for their assigned group of patients.

Changes in nursing skill requirements

When patient care units in hospitals are merged, a redistribution of the patient case mix on these units often follows. As a result, the skill requirements for the nurses providing the patient care frequently change as well. Nurses who were formerly specialists in patient care for a particular case mix are then required to become generalists who are multiskilled at caring for different mixes of patients. As you plan your career, you should consider how multiskilling within nursing can make you more marketable.

Changing roles for unit-level management

The concerted effort to apply business principles to health care is also reflected in the changes that have occurred in the role requirements for the manager of these reconfigured patient care units. Perhaps the most telling evidence of this dramatic shift lies in the unit manager's changed job title. Such titles as "health services manager" or "patient care service leader" imply that the focus of the role is now on management, a skill that may not require nursing preparation. Thus applicants from any number of health-related professional groups or graduates of health care administration programs may fulfil the position's requirements. The belief that a nurse is the best manager of patient care on a unit is being threatened and with it, one of the traditional career options for nurses. In today's health care environment, a nurse who is interested in a management role must compete for it along with a variety of other health care professionals. Of course, this change also opens up other opportunities for nurses to compete for management positions previously occupied by non-nurses.

Part-time and casual employment trends

In the past, part-time and flexible work options had sometimes been the "choice" of nurses who wanted a mechanism for balancing work and family life. The element of choice, however, is important to consider. In today's health care market, that choice is being driven by the employer. Many nurses are not being offered the option of full-time or part-time work; the only choice available is part-time. The rationale behind this current trend towards part-time and casual employment in health care is of interest. These workers cost the health care system less in terms of salary, benefits, and vacation. They are employed on a shift-by-shift basis according to need, which suggests variable or inconsistent utilization patterns. Furthermore, nurses often float between units filling in the gaps across a number of settings. Job insecurity is prevalent for these nurses because they do not know how much work they will get on a week-to-week basis. These changes in employment patterns have challenging implications for nurses' career development options.

Emergence of unregulated staff mix models

The use of unregulated workers, whom organizations have introduced to further contain costs, has darkened the already threatening career picture. The media is crowded with examples of regulated professional staff, such as registered nurses, who were laid off only to be replaced by unregulated workers. The literature demonstrates that this pattern also occurred in the U.S. with the employment of unlicensed assistive workers. Yet many researchers have identified concern that these new staff mix models have not been evaluated. In fact, one of the few staff mix models to be examined empirically in the literature recently has been found to be more costly in terms of salary, supply costs, and productivity (Lengacher et al., 1996). What is unclear in the Canadian experience with these staff mix models is the scope of the work that these unregulated workers are performing. Some organizations suggest they are employed to perform non-nursing work, while others indicate that they carry out some direct patient care activities. The use of unregulated workers has implications for nurses who not only have taken on the management of patient care on the units in the absence of managers, but are now taking on the management of new workers as well.

Changes in patient acuity

A significant change to occur in the workplace can be associated with the decrease in patient length of stay. Recovering patients are sent home earlier with instructions given out on discharge to help them manage their recovery at home. The patients remaining in the hospital need to be there. They are there because they are labour intensive and require treatments, monitoring, and therapy that cannot be provided at home. Nurses observe that patients' acuity has increased. While that may be the case, it is somewhat difficult to distinguish since there are no longer so called "lighter" patients in hospitals to balance the assignment levels. Whether or not they are more acutely ill is not known, although the perception of in-hospital patients' being sicker prevails.

Changes in the employee-employer relationship

This change, which is pervasive at the workplace level, is perhaps also the biggest system-wide change that has influenced nursing and health care and is part of the general global reorganization of work. Some of the reasons for changes to the relationship involve the high costs associated with the allocation of human resources; others relate to the introduction of technology or to evolving social values. The old relationship was long-term and full-time; reward for performance was a promotion, loyalty guaranteed a lifetime career; and experience and education were key factors in upward mobility. Nurses in the old relationship entered an organization with the confidence that if they remained loyal and did their work satisfactorily, they would have a position for life. Indeed, organizations had a variety of lower stress, less physical roles, such as procedure manual coordinator or staffing coordinator, that were available to older, loyal nurse employees. These positions no longer exist. In the new relationships, roles and positions are situational, systems are temporary, and positions are often short-term, contract, or part-time. Reward for performance is acknowledgement of contribution, loyalty means responsibility and good work, and rapidly evolving skills are needed. Nurses are employed for the work that needs doing, with little guarantee of longevity in the organization.

These changes, while stressful and frightening for nurses, have also provided a liberating opportunity. Although there may have been a sense of security in the old dependent relationship, there was also lack of freedom to determine one's own future. The new relationship can provide opportunities to enhance control over your future.

Implications of the Environmental Scan for Registered Nurses

Nursing as knowledge work

Health care reforms and the resulting changes to the health care system and the workplace provide a unique set of challenges for the registered nurse. Despite all of the restructuring and redesign initiatives that have taken place, the one thing to remain constant is the role that the registered nurse has in the provision of patient care. While there have been some structural changes made within health care that appear to devolve the role of nurses in the health care system, these may in effect lead to a more substantive recognition of the importance of the registered nurse's role in patient care delivery. As consumers become more educated and involved in patient care within this reformed system, they will demand more in-depth explanations of their care processes and of outcomes that they can expect to achieve. Answers to these questions will require knowledge.

Drucker (1980) suggested that the workforce is composed of two segments of workers: knowledge workers and service workers. Knowledge workers are those with fairly advanced educations who perform highly specialized tasks and enjoy unlimited mobility compared to service workers. The registered nurse is fast becoming the knowledge worker in our reformed health care system.

Nursing as professional skilled practice
As patient length of stay decreases and the patients remaining in hospital are perceived to be more acutely ill, they will require care from individuals who are educated and highly competent in terms of skill and expertise. Unregulated workers cannot provide the necessary skills required to care for these patients. As well, in the new organizational structures, care providers have limited direction, guidance, or supervision from their managers. Support roles that existed in former care delivery models have been deleted. Staff responsible for patient care will be required to be independent, autonomous thinkers, who are capable of making decisions on their own, have experience doing so, and have been educated to do so as part of their professional practice.

Asserting nursing's role
One of the challenges for registered nurses is the fragmented employment pattern that exists in the current economy. But considering the increased level of patient involvement in the health care system, patients may soon respond to the lack of continuity and inconsistency in treatment and care planning that occurs when a full-time labour force is not utilized. From the patients' perspective, the use of temporary or part-time workers may prove more costly than cost efficient.

Patients also value and recognize registered nurses for their knowledge. It does not really matter whether nursing is nestled within its own division, programs, or in patient groupings within an organizational structure. Registered nurses are the only care providers who possess the knowledge and skill to support the new structures that have been created in response to these system reforms.

Unfortunately, a great deal of unwarranted anxiety, some of it suffered by registered nurses, exists in the current health care environment regarding the replacement of registered nurses with unregulated workers. Some of the confusion for registered nurses arises from the perception of the simultaneous laying off of nurses and the emergence of support worker roles in redesign initiatives. But while it is true that unregulated workers exist in health care institutions, for the most part they are performing unit-related, non-nursing care activities, which are not within the domain of professional nursing practice. The need for these workers evolved in response to the nursing shortage of the 1980s, when registered nurses clearly stated that they no longer wanted to perform non-nursing activities. There is no doubt that unregulated workers are here to stay. The task for nursing is to monitor the extent of the unregulated workers' role in relation to patient care and examine what activities are being delegated to them.

Rather than approaching system reforms as battles for turf, registered nurses should realize that the challenge facing them is not whether they will have a role in the redefined health care system, but whether and how they will determine what they want that role to be. Therefore, in an era of cost constraint, the nursing role must be seen as both cost effective and efficient. Moreover, it is essential that registered nurses move away from thinking of the profession of nursing as a job. Nursing is a career that provides opportunities for growth and lifelong learning.

Scanning as a Nursing Activity

Scanning the health care environment is the first step that you can take to prepare for future health care changes. You should begin your environmental scan by examining global health care trends and then narrow your focus to analyze system level changes in the environment at the national and regional level. Finally, you should scan the changes occurring at the more specific workplace level by examining how restructuring has affected the role of the nurse executive, patient care delivery, nursing skill requirements, and the roles of unit-level managers. Scanning changes in employee-employer relationships that are consequences of such trends as part-time and casual employment, the emergence of a variety of staff mix models, and changes in patient acuity will provide you with an orientation to the current realities of the work world. You should remember to conduct this scan under the premises that nursing is knowledge work and a professional skilled practice and that the need to assert nursing's role in a reformed health system must be recognized. The trends and issues you identify in your scan will serve as a basis for you to make informed decisions about career options and then to plan strategically to implement them. But before you begin to put your plan into place, you need to turn your sights inward and complete a thorough self-assessment.

REFERENCES

Baker, G. R. (1992). Changing patterns of governance for hospitals: Issues and models. In R. B. Deber & G. G. Thompson (Eds.), *Restructuring Canada's health services system: How do we get there from here?* (pp. 195-206). Toronto, Ontario: University of Toronto Press.

Dagnone, T. (1996, November). *A wake-up call for integrated delivery networks and information technology.* Paper presented at the Ontario Hospital Association Convention, Toronto, Ontario.

Drucker, P. (1980). *Managing in turbulent times.* New York: Harper & Row.

Epp, J. (1986). *Achieving health for all: A framework for health promotion.* Ottawa, Ontario: Health and Welfare Canada.

Hammer, M., & Champy, J. (1993). *Reengineering the corporation.* New York: Harper Collins.

Lalonde, M. (1974). *A new perspective on the health of Canadians.* Ottawa, Ontario: Government of Canada.

Leatt, P., Baker, G. R., Halverson, P. K., & Aird, C. (1997). Downsizing, reengineering, and rightsizing: Long-term implications for healthcare organizations. *Frontiers of Health Services Management, 13*(4), 3-37.

Lengacher, C. A., Mabe, P. R., Heinemann, D., Van Cott, M. L., Swymer, S., & Kent, K. (1996). Effects of the PIPC model on outcome measures of productivity and costs. *Nursing Economic$, 14,* 205-213.

McGillis Hall, L. (1997). Staff mix models: Complementary or substitution roles for nurses. *Nursing Administration Quarterly, 21*(2), 31-39.

Naylor, C. D., Anderson, G. M., & Goel, V. (1994). *Patterns of health care in Ontario.* Toronto, Ontario: Institute for Clinical Evaluative Sciences in Ontario.

Rachlis, M., & Kushner, C. (1994). *Strong medicine: How to save Canada's health care system.* Toronto, Ontario: Harper Collins.

Shortell, S. M., Gillies, R. R., Anderson, D. A., Erickson, K. M., & Mitchell, J. B. (1996). *Remaking health care in America: Building organized delivery systems.* San Francisco, CA: Jossey-Bass.

Sutherland, R. W., & Fulton, M. J. (1992). *Health care in Canada: A description and analysis of Canadian health services.* Ottawa, Ontario: The Health Group.

CHAPTER THREE

Completing Your Self-Assessment and Reality Check

Gail J. Donner, RN, PhD[1]

W hen you scanned the environment, you focused on notic-
ing what surrounds you and on understanding what that
told you about the present and the future, as well as about
potential career opportunities. Now as you begin your self-assessment, you will turn to focus on yourself so that you can recognize,
first, all the attributes that make you who you are and, then, what
you in turn have to offer to the environment. Completing your self-
assessment will allow you to give honest and accurate answers to the
two questions, "*Who am I?*" and "*How am I seen?*" When put together with the results of your environmental scan, your replies will
enable you to complete the last two phases of the career planning
and development process: creating your career vision and developing
your strategic career plan to realize that vision. Scanning your environment and completing your self-assessment and reality check are
pivotal to being able to ask yourself that final question, "*What, then,
shall I plan to do?*"

1. The author would like to thank Rilla E. Clark, MSc for her invaluable assistance
with the development of the content of this chapter.

In this chapter we will address the process of self-assessment, why it is important, and how to accomplish it. Like scanning, self-assessment should not be a one-time activity, but rather a continuous part of your personal and professional development. The sooner you begin a systematic process of self-assessment, whether you are in your first year of nursing or are an experienced practitioner, the more attuned and meaningful will be the match between you and the work you do.

Why Do A Self-Assessment?

In today's competitive job market, individuals are expected not only to recognize their skills but also to take the initiative to market these skills to prospective employers. Before they hire you, employers want to examine, in more depth than ever before, who you are and what you can do for them. You now need to be able to articulate your accomplishments clearly and persuasively so that they also reveal your values, skills, and interests. But as Scherer (1993, p.8) said, "Real value can only be given by people who know their own value. How can any of us know our true value if we never take inventory?" That is what completing a self-assessment does; it involves giving yourself the time and permission to concentrate and look inward, to take stock, and to develop a personal and professional profile. Self-assessment requires considerable reflection, the ability to ask yourself some hard questions, and the determination to validate your responses with others.

Over the years you may have haphazardly gathered some impressions about what you liked or disliked doing and have some sense of your abilities and limitations. You may also have developed in many ways outside your professional arena. After all these experiences, who you are now may be very different from who you were when you chose to pursue a career in nursing. But without a deliberate self-assessment, you would have only a fuzzy picture at best of your current self. How, then, could you know what you would want and are best able to do now, let alone how to take control to direct your future? If you neglect this phase in the career planning and development process, you will be driven only by the needs of the market or the opinions of others. The result is often dissatisfaction with the job chosen or poor performance because your values, skills, and interests do not match the job requirements. For example, without completing a thorough self-assessment, Carlotta, a staff nurse, would have no accurate way of determining whether her 8 years of experience in the Neonatal Intensive Care Unit actually suited her to become the nurse manager in that unit. She knew that just because she did an excellent job at the bedside, it did not necessarily follow that she had the values, skills, and interests required to perform successfully in a management position.

Although completing a self-assessment is a process that takes time, the result is a better awareness of yourself and your strengths and limitations. The process will help you learn about which facets of yourself have remained unexpressed or untapped and how to develop them. Moreover, you will begin to understand how you may have been limited by learned perceptions, familiar but unsatisfying roles, or others' expectations of you. You will then be better able to capitalize on your strengths and life experiences.

Make sure that your self-assessment is comprehensive. As Foord Kirk (1997) cautioned, employers are now paying particular attention to job candidates' so-called "soft skills," that is, how they deal with others and handle difficult situations and what their drive and enthusiasm are like. In the past, job requirements tended to relate only to job duties, or "hard skills," not to work attitudes. She suggested that, when you sit down to evaluate your skills and abilities and to assess what you have to sell in today's workplace, you take into account your personality and nature, your attitude, the way you work with others, and your ease of communication. These attributes are as important as your clinical skills. Recognizing what these skills are and the degree to which you possess them are also crucial outcomes of the self-assessment process.

Once you have completed your self-assessment, you will be able to promote what you have to offer and understand where to improve or add to your skills. With an accurate picture of yourself to add to your environmental scan, you will be able to investigate the full spectrum of available opportunities and decide which options are the right ones for you. Your confidence and self-esteem will soar.

COMPLETING YOUR SELF-ASSESSMENT

Who Am I?

Answering this question involves much more than describing what you do or what your job title is. Work is just one part of our lives, but regrettably many people describe who they are only in relation to the work they do. Even though we spend a considerable amount of time at a job, we cannot ignore those other components that complete our lives, including our health, financial resources, friends, family, and community. As you move through your self-assessment, you need to keep the whole you in mind. Think, for instance, about all the adjectives you could use to detail what makes you unique. Although we are all unique, all special, the challenge lies in being able to articulate that uniqueness.

For many nurses, these are not easy activities. How often have you overheard a colleague, when asked the question, "Tell me about yourself," respond with, "Oh, I'm just a nurse." But no one is "just" anything. We are complex human beings, the sum of our past and current experiences, whose selves are composed of mind, body, emotions, and spirit. Maslow (1970) coined the term, *self-actualization*, meaning the ability to realize one's potential capacities by becoming involved in pursuits that engage all four aspects of self in a balanced way that leads to a meaningful life.

Who we are includes our beliefs and values, our skills, and our interests. Beliefs are the way we view ourselves and the world around us. Values are a set of beliefs that drive our decisions, actions, behaviours, and relations. They are the ideals that guide and give meaning to our lives and work. Skills are the abilities and behaviours we use to produce results, and interests are the activities in which we like to spend most of our time and from which we gain pleasure.

Having completed a self-assessment to discover who you are is like looking at a tapestry, rich in the colours and designs that reflect all of you. It will show you where you have been and where you are now, both personally and professionally. But just as your self will continue to unfold and grow in a lifelong process, so too must your self-assessment be a continuous part of your development activities throughout your career as new experiences are woven into the ever growing tapestry.

Beginning the Process

As you proceed with your self-assessment, you will begin to recognize some common themes and patterns that have shaped who you are and what you do. You will also be able to clearly identify what you value and what are your interests, special talents, and abilities. Then you can begin to spot any lack of congruence between them and your current activities and, perhaps, start to get a picture of where you may like to be in the future.

The following are some preliminary questions that can help you understand who you are and what is important to you. They should not limit you but act as a catalyst to start your reflections. Your answers will give you the words to describe your unique self, what you like to do, and what you have to offer. Record your responses in a journal so that you have tangible evidence of who you are. As you start to document your answers, you can begin to write your own story: where you have been, where you are now, and what you have learned about yourself along the way. Your story should include all the important personal and professional events in your life and how they relate to one another. As you write your story, envision that you are writing a book, your autobiography. What would you call it? Could you locate the chapter you are in now, and what title would you give it? As you move forward in the career planning and development process, keep your journal handy to consult and to add or delete information as needed.

Assessing your values

Values are those principles we prize, cherish, or esteem, those beliefs we hold as extremely important. Values direct our decisions and influence our lives. Psychologists suggest that ultimate satisfaction comes from living and working in concert with our values. As you begin to identify your values, consider which ones are present in your current job and which ones are not. Three questions will help you get started: (a) What is important to me in my job and in my personal life?; (b) Where are my priorities – self, family, community, or other?; and (c) Who or what are the significant things in my life that I need to consider at this time? For example, if you are at a stage in your personal life where you are considering starting a family, you should think about how this decision will affect your career. If your workplace is expanding the role of manager so that it no longer includes a clinical component, you need to consider whether that is still congruent with what you believe the role of a manager should be. Finally, if the opportunity to learn is important to you, a workplace that offers means of continuing your education, either formally or informally, will be of greater value to you.

Assessing your skills

Skills are developed or acquired abilities. There are three general categories of skills: (a) technical or job content or "hard skills," such as those involved with providing total nursing care to neonates; (b) managerial skills, which concern communication, coordination, or support; and (c) personal traits, such as adaptability, energy, or logical reasoning. Managerial skills and personal traits would be considered "soft skills," which often are highly transferable.

In this component of the self-assessment process, you should evaluate both your hard and soft skills and understand what you have to offer a potential employer. Take some time to reflect over your whole career and to consider the most significant highlights or milestones along the way. Consider not only the professional work you have done, but also your personal and community life. Identifying the skills you acquired will enable you to clarify what you have to offer and to determine which skills can be transferred to other settings. Skills such as case management, documentation, problem solving, and crisis management are generic skills that can easily be transferred to a variety of roles and organizations, both within and outside of health care. Which of your skills require further development? Skill gaps or limitations are just as important to acknowledge as your strengths. If you do not recognize these limitations and act to address them, you may assume roles for which you are ill suited and, thereby, inhibit your ability to succeed.

Assessing your interests

Interests provide another measure of "fit" between what a job provides and what we'd ideally like to be doing. They can be grouped into four categories: (a) people – helping, serving, caring for, or selling things to people; (b) data – working with facts, records, or files; (c) things – working with machines, tools, or living things; and (d) ideas – creating insights, theories, or new ways of saying or doing something. Think about the work you have done and the life you have lived. What energizes or motivates you? What do you enjoy in your current work? What haven't you liked? In what kind of environment do you perform at your best? What kind of people do you like to have around you? What habits and styles of learning appeal to you? For instance, if working with technology and equipment challenges and stimulates you, then an opportunity in an organization that is computerizing its nursing documentation will be attractive. However, if people contact most appeals to you, such an environment may not be appropriate. If you like constant change and do not need to establish continuing relationships with clients, then emergency nursing may be an excellent career choice. You must articulate what excites you and makes you feel most alive and fulfilled.

Recognizing your accomplishments

As you finish your self-assessment, you should be able to identify your strengths and limitations as well as your significant accomplishments over the past 5, 10, 15, or more years. The insights and answers to the "who am I?" question can be found in each individual's personal and professional accomplishments. Accomplishments refer to those activities in which you went beyond what you were hired to do. They are not items on a job description. Rather, they are situations where you identified a challenge, used a specific approach, and had a successful outcome. Accomplishments don't have to be a big deal. But they do represent those times in your life that you made a difference. These accomplishments become the value added you bring to any work environment. An accomplishment can be anything from being a member of your child's school's fund raising committee to being elected as the unit representative on a committee or to having an article published; it reflects those times in which you achieved a personal or professional best.

Carlotta's Self-Assessment

My current position is staff nurse, Neonatal Intensive Care Unit (NICU). I graduated from a diploma nursing program, returned to school, and obtained a degree in nursing and a post-basic certificate in neonatal nursing. I am very involved in two community groups, Big Sisters and my church. I have completed a very thorough self-assessment and the following are some highlights from it. I especially value (a) autonomy – the personal freedom to set my own work schedule, (b) variety – of tasks and routines, and (c) team work – frequent interpersonal interactions. My "hard skills" include my clinical expertise in the care of neonates, and my "soft skills" include counselling and supporting families, problem solving in acute-care situations, and collaborating with others on the health care team in the NICU. I am also calm, decisive, flexible, and persuasive. I have an interest in people, particularly newborns, and things, including computer technology. My personal accomplishments include being a Big Sister to a 12-year-old girl and being elected by my peers to my church pastoral committee. My professional accomplishments include identifying breast-feeding information needs of parents with babies in the NICU and then designing a resource package for them. I also sit on our hospital Nurses Week Committee and for the last 2 years have chaired the sub-committee on guest speakers. My strengths include my commitment to quality family-centred care, which is exhibited not only by my excellent nursing skills, but also by my excellent communication and interpersonal skills with parents, whom I support while their child is in the NICU. My other strengths include my ability to work collaboratively with others in both my personal and professional life. My current limitations include my reluctance to write and make presentations about the breast-feeding resource package I developed. Therefore, I have identified two current skill gaps, public speaking and writing for professional journals.

Continuing the Process

It is wise to continue to keep an ongoing record of all personal and professional experiences that have had an impact on your career. It is even better if you annotate this list, that is, make personal notes about what you learned, what you enjoyed or not and why, and how you may wish to follow up on a particular interest or challenge. This journal then will become a working historical document that you can rely on to inform later decisions. Remember that, over time, your life experiences, values, self-knowledge, and goals will change. Not only may your work experience be varied and include different career opportunities within nursing, but your levels of expertise may broaden or become highly specialized. Over the years, you will also develop in many ways outside the professional arena. People's vocational interests change and grow; family commitments change, demanding more or less attention; beliefs and values become clearer. Documenting such personal and professional history will provide you with an inventory of inner resources which will serve you well as you develop an ongoing career plan that will be realistic and fulfilling.

YOUR REALITY CHECK: ASKING, "HOW AM I SEEN?"

Once you have completed your self-assessment, you must validate it. "How do others see me?" is the complementary and critical question you must ask yourself next. Careful career planning requires feedback, both formal and informal, from managers, peers, friends, and family. You may derive this feedback from routine performance appraisals as well as from ongoing dialogue and discussion about your current performance and future possibilities. Asking for feedback is not easy, but successful career planning depends on your being open to new ideas and perspectives. It involves listening and accepting positive feedback and acknowledging those areas where change is needed. Seeking advice about new skills that you may require and how to develop them is essential too.

Re-read your accomplishments from your journal. Now reflect on what feedback you have received about these achievements from your peers, manager, staff, friends, and family. Did anyone else know about what you considered an accomplishment? Nurses often have been hesitant to boast about what they have accomplished and how they have made a difference. It feels uncomfortable.

Getting feedback affirms where we shine. But before others can give us feedback, they need to know that we are open to hearing what will be said. Start with those individuals you trust. What three adjectives would they use to describe you, both in and outside your workplace, and why? What would they identify as your strengths and limitations? Now consider getting feedback from an individual whom you know, but not that well, and ask her or him the same questions. Asking such sources for feedback may be risky, but their responses will further enhance your self-assessment. You can also refer to any performance reviews, notes of appreciation, or personal notes you may have taken when you received feedback.

Be aware of how people have evaluated your strengths and limitations. So called "360 degree feedback," that is, feedback from all levels of people with whom you work, is essential to deepening your levels of self-awareness and facilitating your growth. You need a range of opinion in order to approximate the objective truth. No one welcomes criticism; yet, when it is delivered and received constructively and in the context of a caring relationship which encourages growth and self-development, it can be instrumental in your career. For instance, you may hold an unrealistically high opinion of your attributes, which can lead to your setting your sights on a particular job and being continually disappointed because you are not selected. Or, alternatively, you may have an unrealistically low opinion of your attributes, which may prevent you from seeking positions well within your reach or lead to your selling yourself short in your current role. So be prepared to invite and listen carefully to feedback and to acknowledge those areas in yourself where change is needed. Ask for input about how to develop new skills and attitudes.

Carlotta's Reality Check

> To get feedback on my accomplishments, I developed a list of all those who could possibly give me feedback. The list included the Executive Director, Big Sisters, and my "little sister"; the Chair of the Pastoral Committee and three members of the committee; my nurse manager, the neonatologist, three of my peers, and two families I am currently working closely with in the NICU; and the Chair of the Nurses Week Committee. Out of this list, I chose five individuals, met with them, and asked them what three adjectives they would use to describe me and why. I was pleased with the responses, which included the following three strengths: that I was caring – showing concern for people, that I was a creative problem solver – seeing many alternatives, and that I was persistent – I stick to tasks. Two individuals identified the same limitations, that I appear hesitant to speak in public about my accomplishments and that I have so much to offer but often my accomplishments go unnoticed.

OTHER RESOURCES

At most times during your career, you will be able to complete the self-assessment and reality check on your own, that is, using friends, family, and colleagues to help. There may, however, be circumstances in which you require additional professional assistance. You may, for instance, have scanned your environment and completed your self-assessment and reality check and realized that you are still quite confused and unclear about where your strengths lie and the nature of your limitations. Or, you may feel that your environment is complex and that you are at a particular fork in your career path where taking a different direction seems desirable, but you are not sure you have identified your own abilities and skills carefully enough to decide where to go. It is in these circumstances that you may wish to consult a career counsellor and have yourself assessed in a more formal and comprehensive way. Undergoing such a process will help you understand your attributes in a detailed manner and then direct you to specific related career paths, which may diverge from or intersect with your current path.

If the services of a professional are required to complement your self-assessment, the counsellor can rely on a variety of well researched and developed instruments to help you assess your strengths, traits, and characteristics in an objective way and relative to the work environment. It is very helpful to familiarize yourself with the spectrum of assessment materials and then decide which ones to take and whom to entrust with the administration, scoring, feedback, and implementation follow up. Standardized tests, in combination with your ongoing self-assessment, may change your perceptions and open doors to new roles or settings within nursing or in alternate careers. Such standardized tests are designed to measure cognitive intelligence (e.g., Wechsler Adult Intelligence Scale-Revised [WAIS-R]), multiple intelligences (e.g., MI Inventory), emotional intelligence (e.g., EQ-i), personality (e.g., Myers-Briggs Type Indicator [MBTI]), interests (e.g., Campbell Interest and Skills Survey [CISS]), and lifestyle needs and values (e.g., Adult Balanced Life Enhancement Inventory [ABLE]). Testing services may be available to you at no cost through an Employee Assistance Program, the Internet, or at a career development centre associated with your workplace, a relocation or outplacement firm, your local university or community college, or the YM/YWCA. Do your research and select a professional who is a career development specialist.

PUTTING IT ALL TOGETHER

Success and satisfaction depend on having the courage, confidence, and will to express who you are congruently in your work. Self-assessment provides you with the means to do this. Whether you conduct a self-assessment independently or with the help of a professional career counsellor, you will be able to recognize and appreciate your full range of inner resources: intelligences, interests, personality, values, and motivations. The more research you do, the more thorough and realistic your findings will be. Your performance reviews and conversations with peers and managers with whom you have worked will serve as reality checks to deepen your self-knowledge. Take time to collect constructive feedback and think it over carefully. Piece together all the data now to create a written, composite profile of your strengths and challenges. This document will serve as your passport to the new land of career research and enable you to negotiate the last two phases of the career planning and development process: creating your career vision and developing a strategic plan to achieve it. With an accurate sense of who you are and how others see you, you will be ready to explore job descriptions, physical and emotional environments, working conditions, and benefits to determine where you would have the most to contribute. Revisiting your self-assessment throughout your life span will allow you to update your knowledge of self, set learning goals, develop career goals and action plans, and feel confident that you will love the work you do. Knowledge of your personal resources is a form of capital that represents an effective investment in your future. Use it and you will be the one who is in charge of your career, both now and in the future.

REFERENCES

Foord Kirk, J. (1997, November 1). Soft skills needed for most types of jobs. *The Toronto Star*, p. H1.

Maslow, A. (1970). *Motivation and personality* (2nd ed.). New York: Harper & Row.

Scherer, J. (1993). *Work and the human spirit*. Spokane, WA: John Scherer & Associates.

FURTHER READING

Bridges, W. (1997). *Creating you & co*. Reading, MA: Addison-Wesley.

Covey, S. (1989). *The seven habits of highly effective people*. New York: Simon & Schuster.

Kolbe, K. (1991). *The conative connection*. Reading, MA: Addison-Wesley.

Moses, B. (1997). *Career intelligence: Mastering the new work and personal realities*. Toronto, Ontario: Stoddart.

Schein, E. (1990). *Discovering your real values* (2nd ed.). San Francisco: Pfeiffer & Co.

Tieger, P., & Tieger, B. (1995). *Do what you are*. Boston: Little, Brown and Company.

CHAPTER FOUR

Creating Your Career Vision

Mary M. Wheeler, RN, MEd

Mary M. Wheeler is President of Mary M. Wheeler & Associates, a consulting firm specializing in organization and human resource development with a special interest in the human side of change. She is also a Partner in Donner & Wheeler and Associates, a consulting firm specializing in career planning and development within the health and social service sectors. Mary has been self-employed since 1991.

You may be most familiar with the term *vision* when it is used to refer to a component of an organization's strategic planning process. An organization scans its external environment to ascertain where opportunities or threats may be and looks internally to assess its strengths and limitations. Then the organization creates a vision statement that describes the direction in which it wants to go in the future, and it develops action plans to ensure that its vision becomes a reality. Individual nurses need to use a similar process to ensure that the career visions they create become a reality.

In Chapters Two and Three, we showed you how to use the first two phases of our career planning and development process, *Scanning Your Environment* and *Completing Your Self-Assessment and Reality Check.* These phases are fairly concrete, but the third, *Creating Your Career Vision*, is somewhat more abstract, and its concepts harder to grasp. Creating a career vision is that point in the process where you integrate what you learned from your environmental scan with your self-assessment, and you begin to formulate an idea of what you want to do with your nursing career by taking a more active than passive role in your career development. In this chapter you will learn about what is involved in the concept of career vision, why it is important to have one, and how to go about creating one of your own. You will also learn how to determine what your career options may be at any given time and how to set your short- and long-term goals. In the next chapter, Anne Coghlan will show you how to develop a strategic plan to ensure that you reach those goals.

CAREER VISIONS

Vision is another word for a dream, an image of potentiality. A career vision is tempered by the realities of your environmental scan and self-assessment, but not determined by them. Those who have a career vision talk in terms of what is possible. They make use of all their resources, and they have the ability to harness and focus their energy. Having a career vision is perhaps the most forceful motivator for change that individuals can possess.

Dreaming is the beginning of all human endeavours. Unless you can dream, how do you know where you want to go? And until you know where you want to go, how can you sit down and plan how to get there? Dreams can be incredibly fragile, but individuals need to be encouraged to dream. You may say, "Why bother?," but if you do not, what could you be missing out on? How would you know what your real potential is? Lindaman and Lippitt (1979) pointed out that the choice is crucial, whether to cope reactively to a future created by others or to work creatively and strategically to craft a future you prefer. But in order to shape that future, you must hold an image in your mind of what it is that you really want. It is this use of imagination, whether initiated by idle dreaming or conscious intention, that will propel you into the future.

Bridges (1994) observed that most successful organizations are made up of people doing what they like to do and believe in doing, rather than of people doing what they are "supposed to" (p.78). Remember back to when you chose nursing as a career. You had formed some kind of picture of what nursing would look like and what part you would play in it. You created that ideal vision for your work and your future. Yet over the years both you and the realities of the workplace may have undergone a significant change. Therefore, you should be continuously reassessing whether that first picture still accurately depicts your current reality: "Am I still feeling the way I felt when I chose nursing as a career, still doing what I want to be doing?"

Bridges (1994) encourages us to ask ourselves the questions, "What do I really want to do?" and "What do I want so badly that I would do almost anything to achieve it?" People who desire something discover talents they never knew they had. They argue their case so persuasively (because they believe in it) that they gain allies, and they solve problems that in any other setting they would have considered insoluble. When you are trying to decide what you are going to do next in your life, what you really desire is the only valid place to begin. Desire is the first and most important ingredient of the powerful motivation that is essential to career success.

The dramatic changes happening in today's workplace mean that nurses can no longer count on a nursing job for life in one organization as a sure thing. In the future, success will rest on your adaptability, your ability and commitment to embrace change, and on your assuming the active management of your own career. Change, although frightening and intimidating, can also be very rewarding. Embracing change means pushing yourself to explore all the possibilities, for unless you take some risks, you really never will know the extent of your potential. The question no longer is, "Can I change?," but "What kind of change do I want?" That is what creating a career vision does; it answers the question, "What do I want?" If you do not have some idea of where you want to go, you more often will just be reacting to events as they occur rather than choosing a direction in which to go. Nor will you easily be able to recognize and take advantage of an opportunity when it occurs.

Many nurses have never considered that they could have a part to play in designing their career futures. Some may have to free themselves from a career path that others have expected of them before they can begin to formulate their own career vision. Other nurses will have to acknowledge that they have more choices than they had ever considered. These changes require a shift in orientation. You must move from being the observer about what "they" think you should be doing with your career to becoming an active participant in the picture, a goal setter, a doer. That means taking control of your career and your future, making choices, understanding the consequences, and moving forward.

Today, career success is dependent not only on having a dream, but on knowing how to turn that dream into a reality. Creating a career vision is the first step in that process. If followed by determining career options, setting goals, and developing a strategic plan, it can lead you to success, whether good times or bad lie ahead.

CREATING YOUR CAREER VISION

Wouldn't it be great to create your work the way you want it? You can, but first you need to create a vision for your work. It may be a more fulfilling version of what you are already doing, or it may be very different. Creating a career vision begins with taking time to do some active daydreaming about an ideal day in your future. Your career vision will be as individual as you are. Creating it will require you to ask yourself some important questions, and give yourself permission to let go of what you previously thought possible. Sher (1983) asked, "Do you wake up every morning excited about the day ahead and delighted to be doing what you're doing, even if you're sometimes a little nervous and scared?" If not, what would make it that way for you? What is your fondest dream? Whatever it is, "as of right now I want you to start taking it very, very seriously!" (Sher, p. xi).

When you start, your vision doesn't have to be too realistic; that comes later in the process when you determine your options and set your career goals. Don't worry about your vision's being too big, too vague, or too impossible. It should be grand, inspiring, and if it is an important dream, it may be a little scary. Hopkins (1986) said that when ancient mariners set off across uncharted waters to discover the lands of their dreams, their maps warned, "Here Be Dragons" (p.10). If you want to pursue your dreams, you too must be prepared to go where the dragons are.

You should begin creating your career vision by recognizing that you can have your work be all that you envision. "How can I become the best I can be; how can I combine my skills and talents with my dreams?" With a clear career vision, firm commitment, and the knowledge to bring it about, you will embark on a journey to discover your full potential.

The following questions may guide you in the process of creating a career vision of your ideal work. The first set of questions, **Where**

would I like to go?, functions like a warm-up or brainstorming session. Blue sky thinking is at work here; no answer is wrong. The second set of questions, **What is my ideal vision for my work?**, provides more focus as you begin to create your career vision. As you answer the questions, your evolving career vision should be influenced rather than determined by the data you gleaned from scanning your environment and completing your self-assessment. As you create your career vision, reflect on what would it be like if it came to pass. What would be the advantages and disadvantages? Then consider what some possible scenarios would be if you didn't move towards what you really wanted to do. Again ask yourself, what would be the advantages and then the disadvantages of not pursuing your career vision? At this point you still have the ability to manoeuvre, to decide how comfortable the career vision feels. All three phases of the career planning and development process begin to merge at this point, and by the time you set your career goals, your career vision should be grounded in reality.

Find a quiet space where you will be undisturbed. Sit in a comfortable chair, and if you like, put on some relaxing music. After each question, close your eyes so you can connect more easily with your imagination and creativity. When you are ready, record your responses in a journal. Formulate your career vision in the present tense, as if it were occurring right now, and in as much descriptive detail as possible.

Where Would I Like to Go?
- What do I want? What am I seeking?
- How do I want to be?
- Is there something that needs doing, that I know something about, that probably won't happen unless I take responsibility for it?
- Where could I make a difference?
- How do I want to live my life and have my work be a part of my life?
- If I didn't have to work for money, what kind of work would I do? Why?
- What do I care about so much that I would pay to do it?

What is My Ideal Vision for My Work?
- In my ideal vision for my work, what does it look like?
- What am I doing, and why do I want to do it?
- Where am I located?
- How is the work structured?
- Who am I working with?
- What are the values by which I am operating?
- What talents and gifts am I using and expressing?
- How am I being acknowledged?
- Is someone currently doing the kind of work I want to do? Describe what you think his or her worklife must be like.

As you moved through the process, you may have come to the point where you said to yourself, "I want to (fill in your own response), but *I can't* because I'm too old, or I don't know how to go about applying for the position, or I'm not good enough." Many nurses do not believe that they can do what they really want to in their careers. These self-limiting beliefs, in particular fear, block us and our progress. They are the old entrenched beliefs that oppose a new idea. What we believe about ourselves and what could be possible are powerful determinants of our behaviour. That is why it is so important to explore our assumptions and clarify the values that underpin them. Pay attention to these self-limiting beliefs because they have the potential to inhibit your ability to create what you want.

According to Gershon and Straub (1989), what we believe is what we create. We must clear our self-limiting beliefs before we can realize new beliefs, and in order to realize new beliefs, we must have a clear vision of what we want to create. They suggest using three techniques: (a) affirmation, or creating a statement of what we want to create in our life; (b) visualization, or forming a mental picture or image of what we want to create; and (c) germination, or the energizing process, that is, being committed to a vision we believe will occur and doing what it takes to make it happen. Talbot (1994) built on the visualization step and suggested that individuals pretend it is a year from today, and they have become very successful (however they define successful). Visualize this success; make a picture and describe it. Then describe the steps that were taken to get there.

Meghan, for example, is a staff nurse currently working on an obstetrical unit in labour and delivery at an acute care teaching hospital. She has an interest in eventually working in the community. When she scanned her external environment, two important trends presented themselves: the shift in health care from hospitals to community and the lack of continuity of care for mothers and babies that resulted from shorter hospital stays. Meghan observed that many of these mothers were returning to the emergency department shortly after discharge with complaints of their infants' failure to thrive and dehydration. When Meghan completed her self-assessment, she recognized not only her expert clinical, education, and people skills, but that she also valued independence, responsibility, the opportunity to influence others, and working as part of a team. She also identified a limitation; she did not have enough experience with newborns. Meghan's ideal vision for her work looks like this:

> *I am working in the community, providing educational services for new mothers and babies. I work in a public health unit with members of an interdisciplinary team. I am being well compensated, including time off for continuing education in the field of community health nursing.*

Yael works as a clinical nurse specialist in psychiatry at a community hospital. When she scanned her environment, she saw that, with hospital restructuring, a new position was about to open up for a nurse manager responsible for a three-site combined psychiatric services program. Prior to her current position, Yael had fulfilled the role of nurse manager on her unit for a 7- month period while the incumbent was away on maternity leave. When Yael completed her self-assessment, she realized that, as the interim nurse manager, she not only liked the role and the responsibilities, but received positive feedback from colleagues, particularly about her supportive relationship with staff on the unit and her leadership in the development of a psychiatric community focus group. She also identified a limitation. Her management experience was only hands on. She had limited formal management education, particularly in the area of financial planning. Yael's ideal vision for her work looks something like this:

I am a nurse manager, providing strategic direction for the development of the new programs in psychiatry at the regional level. I am coaching staff in their new roles as direct service providers, and am working as a valuable member of the newly appointed regional senior management team.

Caitlin was teaching oncology nursing full-time in a university nursing program. Six months ago she took an academic administrative position, which decreased her teaching load but increased her broader departmental responsibilities. Caitlin has two young children. As the result of her self-assessment, particularly in the beliefs and values component, she acknowledged that she was unhappy, that she was unable to manage her workload and still maintain a healthy family life with two young children at home, and that her passion was teaching not management. Her greatest joys came from spending time with her children and from working with nursing students, helping them realize their potential. Caitlin's ideal vision for her work looks like this:

I have relinquished my administrative responsibilities and I am now teaching part-time. I have more time and energy for both my children and my students.

Your career vision may be a confirmation that you're already doing what you love or it may be a revelation of a whole new way to think about expressing yourself in your work. You are more likely to attain satisfying work when you follow your personal passions, pursue your interests, and utilize your strengths. Go back to scanning your environment and your self- assessment. Does your career vision fit with what the new world of work is going to be needing and with the skills, talents, and abilities you have to offer? If so, then you now have a vision of what you want to build, and you can move forward as fast or as slowly as you desire. If not, you haven't wasted your time. Review your scan, self-assessment, and now your career vision. If it still appears realistic, the timing may just not be right. Don't let go of the vision; be patient yet persistent. Make adjustments so that you are positioned to take advantage of better circumstances when the climate changes and the opportunities arise. Surround yourself with those who will support and encourage you when your career vision appears impossible. Talk to some of those individuals, and discuss your career vision with them.

DETERMINING YOUR OPTIONS

Once you have created your career vision, you need to set short- and long-term goals or your vision will remain forever only a dream. But before you do, you have to choose realistic ones. Now that you are able to describe your ideal career vision, it is time to explore possible career options that will not only help you build on existing work experiences, but increase your breadth of skills, enhance your possibilities for future employment, and help you achieve your career vision. What are the possible career options you can choose from to realize your career vision? Identifying work that requires the skills you have and also taps into your interests and values is at the heart of the process.

Determining your career options involves recognizing what may be feasible, clarifying your choices, and making decisions. It is a short but crucial step done right after you create your career vision but just before you set your career goals. These choices or options emerge from the overlap between your environmental scan and your self-assessment. When you were creating your career vision, you kept the information in your scan and self-assessment somewhat in the background so that you did not risk being inhibited and not daring to dream. But now that you have your vision and are determining your career options, the data from your scan and self-assessment should become more influential and assume a place in the foreground of your mind. Which options are viable will vary with changes in the work climate and in yourself; thus, remember the importance of continually scanning your environment and updating your self-assessment.

SETTING YOUR SHORT- AND LONG-TERM CAREER GOALS

Now that you have determined your career options, it is time to set the suitable and practical career goals that will lead you to your vision. A goal is the purpose or objective towards which an endeavour is directed. It keeps you looking towards the future, focused on finishing, on doing it all, and on doing it right. Choosing and setting goals means that you are serious about taking charge of your career.

There are two rules to goal setting. First, a goal must be a concrete action or event. It is a matter of facts, not feelings. Although goals may be related to a specific position, they often are chosen to help you explore different possible pathways towards your career vision. The second basic rule is that when you say, "This is what I want," you mean it. As Sher (1983) pointed out, sometimes there is no way to find out whether or not a particular goal really suits you except by trying it. If it does not, you will still have gained something priceless: the experience of making real progress towards a goal and the practical skills for doing it, skills that can be applied to achieving any goal.

You may choose a combination of short- and long-term goals to transform your career vision into a reality. Moreover, you can concentrate on one goal at a time, pursue two at once, or balance a short and a longer term goal. Pursuing multiple goals encourages flexibility. It helps you feel more in control and less at the mercy of external forces, for example organizational change, so that if your desired direction becomes blocked, you have other options from which to choose.

As Hopkins (1986) said, "A goal is a dream taken seriously" (p.23). The first step to taking your dream seriously is to tell yourself, the second is to set deadlines, and the third is to tell others. When you are choosing your career goals, always ask yourself, "What do I hope to achieve by pursuing this goal?" Remember to keep them specific, time framed, reachable, and relevant. Will anyone who reads them understand what you are trying to accomplish? Do you have actual target dates for achievement? Are your goals realistic enough to be attainable? Are they both stretching and empowering? Are the goals in tune with your future needs?

The three nurses whose career visions were presented earlier all chose a variety of short- and long-term goals as means of realizing their dreams. Meghan, who wanted to work in the community with new mothers and babies, realized she needed post-partum experience. Therefore, her short-term goal was to move to a hospital post-partum unit that has rooming in. Her long-term goal was to move from the hospital to the community and to secure a staff nurse position in either a public health department or a community nursing agency by year-end. Yael, who wanted to work as a nurse manager, chose to pursue two career goals at once. Within the next month, she intended to enroll in a financial planning course at the Business Health Education Centre and to apply for the regional psychiatric nurse manager position. Caitlin, who wanted to return to teaching, set two career goals, one for the short-term and a second for a longer term. The first was to resign from her administrative position within the next week. Then within the next 3 months, she intended to secure a part-time teaching position.

As these examples show, a goal should move you from the intangible to the tangible. Once the goal is written down, say it out loud. What does it sound like? Would you be prepared to share it with others and be open to revising it? When you feel comfortable sharing your career goals and asking for assistance, your network enlarges, and the probability of success increases. How can anyone help you if you do not let them know what you want? You need both to articulate and to own your career goals. The clearer you are about your goals, the easier it will be to develop a plan of action. Remember, career goals should be realistic — I can do it; desirable — I want to do it; and motivating — I will work to make it happen. Be prepared to keep re-evaluating and possibly altering your career goals in order to achieve your career vision. Setting clear goals involves converting your dream from a vague concept into an action-oriented goal statement from which you can design your strategic career plan. Chapter Five will offer more detail about how to accomplish this final phase in the career planning and development process. This next phase will help you answer the question, "How will I get there from here?," and provide you with strategies to close the gap between vision and reality.

REFERENCES

Bridges, W. (1994). *JobShift: How to prosper in a workplace without jobs.* Reading, CT: Addison-Wesley.

Gershon, D., & Straub, G. (1989). *Empowerment: The art of creating your life as you want it.* New York: Dell Publishing.

Hopkins, W. (1986). *A goal is a dream taken seriously.* King of Prussia, PA: The HRD Quarterly.

Lindaman, E., & Lippitt, R. (1979). *Choosing the future you prefer.* Washington, DC: Development Publications.

Sher, B. (1983). *Wishcraft: How to get what you really want.* New York: Ballantine Books.

Talbot, D. A break from the huddle. (1994, August 16). *The Globe and Mail*, p. B20.

FURTHER READING

Edwards, P., & Edwards, S. (1996). *Finding your perfect work: The new career guide to making a living, creating your life.* New York: J. P. Tarcher.

Haldane, B. (1996). *Career satisfaction and success: A guide to job and personal freedom.* Indianapolis, IN: JIST Works.

Jarrow, R. (1995). *Creating the work you love.* Rochester, VT: Destiny Books.

Jones, L. (1996). *The path: Creating your mission statement for work and life.* New York: Hyperion.

Sher, B. (1994). *I could do anything if I only knew what it was.* New York: Dell.

Sinetar, M. (1987). *Do what you love and the money will follow.* New York: Dell.

CHAPTER FIVE

Developing Your Strategic Career Plan

Anne L. Coghlan, RN, MScN

Currently a Principal in the Health Care and Life Sciences Practice of Ernst & Young Management Consultants, Anne Coghlan has held a number of clinical leadership positions in both community hospital and academic health science centre settings. Her interest in career planning started when, as a clinical nurse specialist, she began to explore opportunities for nurses to achieve professional growth and challenge within clinical practice roles.

N
ow that your career vision is clearly articulated, you are ready to move on to the next phase of the career planning process. Developing your strategic career plan is critical to taking control of your own career. Designing a plan is not something that someone else can do for you. You must do it for yourself to ensure that you are continually and satisfactorily progressing towards your personal career goals.

Do you remember the first time you developed a patient care plan? You may recall that care plans initially seemed quite onerous. They required dedicated time, in-depth knowledge of the patient, and a clear understanding of his or her goals. Your own goals and those of the health care team at times may have been confused with patient goals. You also may have experienced developing or reading elaborately designed care plans that for some reason were never implemented! In the end, however, it was worth the effort; the care plan guided you to be able to work in partnership with clients to achieve their health goals. Many similarities can be drawn between developing patient care plans and designing your own strategic career plan. The trick is to ensure that you have a plan that is both uniquely yours and easily converted into action. It must be derived from your career vision and outline specific actions that you can take to achieve clearly defined goals. The motivation to develop a plan comes from genuinely being interested in a career rather than simply being concerned with having regular employment. A career is a lifelong investment and, as with any investment, planning pays off! In this chapter you will learn why nurses develop career plans, what goes into one, and how to use it once you have one.

Why Should I Develop a Career Plan?

Having a plan involves discipline and the ability to measure success. With an effective one, the incremental steps you take to achieve your goals will become recognizable and, when reached, provide you with additional incentives to persevere with your strategic career plan. Think about other kinds of plans that you have used to assist you in achieving a long-term vision. Becoming a home owner, for example, starts with a vision. The potential owner has specific ideas about the location, size, age, and other characteristics of a future home. Specific goals facilitate progress from entertaining dreams to actually living in the desired home. Similarly, specific action plans are required to achieve your vision of a remodeled kitchen. Although it may take years to achieve your vision, the plan helps to ensure that you are continually working in the desired direction. Without having a specific plan for creating the kitchen you originally envisioned, you run the risk of replacing your kitchen windows one year, the floor the next year, and then deciding to relocate the position of your cupboards and appliances only to find that the windows are in the wrong place and that the floor will need replacing.

Developing a career plan is no different. Once you have determined your options and set your short- and long-term goals, the plan you design will help you orchestrate the achievement of your career vision. Without a plan, long-term career goals may appear unattainable or become unattainable. For example, if your career vision is to be a professor in a university nursing program and your short-term goal is to pursue a baccalaureate degree, having a strategic career plan will help you select a program that would also be congruent with your long-term goals and career vision. Without a plan, you may achieve your baccalaureate degree, but it may not position you to succeed, ultimately, in attaining the doctoral degree required of a professor of nursing.

When Should I Start My Career Plan?

It is a bad plan that admits of no modification.
Publilius Syrus, *Maxims*

You should begin as soon as you have created your career vision, determined your options, and set your goals. As you learned in the previous chapter, your options will change throughout your career. Having a strategic career plan ensures that you will be able to build on options that are best suited to achieving your vision. Getting started signals your commitment to acting on a specific goal. It indicates that you are serious about embarking upon the journey towards your overall vision, and that you are ready to address each of the components of an effective plan.

Getting started with your plan requires some dedicated time, energy, and creativity. Don't worry about its being perfect. The best plans start with clear ideas about what both interests you and is possible to achieve. Moreover, your plan will remain effective only if you continually assess whether it still reflects the best means of attaining your goals and vision in light of changes in your environmental scan, self-assessment, or stages of your career.

What Goes Into the Plan?

A strategic career plan includes the identification of goals, action steps, resources, timelines, and indicators of success (Donner & Wheeler, 1993). Document your plan! The exercise of "writing it down" forces you to include each of the critical components and makes it easier for you to continually review, refine, and re-evaluate both your goals and your progress.

TAKING STEPS TO REACH YOUR SHORT-
AND LONG-TERM GOALS

Sometimes the first step you need to take to move you closer to those short- and long-term goals you originally set is to break them down further into smaller, incremental units. Goals that are specific, realistic, and measurable, as well as those that are often subdivided into workable pieces, make your plan more manageable. For instance, a nurse manager, whose career vision was to be a hospital CEO, set becoming a director of nursing as a congruent long-term goal. But then in her strategic plan, she included both shorter term goals that related to securing a director's position and those that also furthered her progress towards her ultimate career vision. Her goal of identifying external opportunities contributed towards her successfully attaining a director's position, while her goal of developing advanced leadership skills was critical to both becoming a director and, ultimately, a CEO.

In another case, a nurse envisioned himself caring for children with special needs in their homes. But because he did not picture himself in a specific job position, his short-term goal was to explore what directions he could take and what qualifications and experience he would require to make his career vision a reality. The first step in his plan was to break that goal down into two more specific and manageable ones: (a) to find out about the requirements and opportunities associated with a nurse practitioner role, and (b) to learn about what would be required to develop administrative expertise.

Action Steps

You can use specific action steps to break goals down further into discrete and concrete activities. Action steps complete the sentence, "In order to achieve this goal, I will ...." For instance, you may have a goal to become more involved in professional activities. The action steps you would plan may include joining a nursing practice committee in your workplace, subscribing to a professional journal, attending chapter meetings, and eventually running for office within your professional organization. The nurse who was pursuing the goal of finding out about the nurse practitioner's role, for example, completed action steps that built upon each other in a planned way. He contacted practising nurse practitioners, got information about entry requirements and the content of education programs, and determined what resources currently exist for a particular patient population.

Remember back again to your first patient care plan. You may have used words like tedious, time consuming, or too theoretical to describe your initial experience with care planning. Chances are you were trying to work with vague, difficult to measure goals. But once those goals were broken down into specific actions, it became much easier to implement the plan and evaluate the outcomes. Similarly, a career plan is most effective when specific, manageable activities form building blocks in the achievement of well defined goals. Action steps the nurse manager interested in a director of nursing role planned included networking to let others know of her interest, preparing her résumé, and getting some coaching to enhance her interview skills. Besides making the goal manageable, she experienced another benefit from having developed concrete actions. As she completed individual action steps, she was able to see tangible evidence of progress towards her overall goal.

MOVING IN DIFFERENT CAREER DIRECTIONS TO ACHIEVE YOUR GOALS

Just as your career plan may involve your working on several complementary goals at once, so too should you consider moving in a variety of career directions to take the most effective action steps you can towards those goals. Career directions, the avenues or pathways you travel on to reach your career vision, exist in organizations and between organizations. Depending on the goals you set and the work climate at the time, one of the following three most popular directions – lateral, vertical, and realignment – will lead you to your goal most successfully.

Remember to be flexible when you consider in which direction to look for appropriate action steps. Let results from your environmental scan and self-assessment, as well as your career stage, be your guide. For instance, where once nurses thought of career development in one way only, towards a promotion, now they may need to consider other career directions that emphasize growth and development without necessitating a furious trip to the top. In today's health care climate, restructuring is creating flatter organizations with even fewer rungs on the ladder to the top. Kaye (1993) coined the phrase, "up is not the only way," (p. 26) before the idea became fashionable. She foresaw a changing business environment where people would need to pursue development not as a ladder upward, but in terms of a variety of moves. Therefore, she argued for a shift in perceiving career success from a vertical to a new, multi-directional paradigm, from a ladder to a lattice.

Lateral — Moving Sideways

A lateral move, or moving sideways, means changing your job but staying at the same level with regard to responsibilities. Taking a lateral career direction is a great way not only to increase your breadth of experience, but to "recharge your batteries" through renewed job satisfaction. In this way, you can seek new experiences and challenges without additional responsibilities and pressures. For instance Meghan, the nurse mentioned in the previous chapter who worked on a labour and delivery unit, chose an action step that took her in a lateral career direction. She sought a position in the hospital's postpartum unit as a means of achieving her short-term goal, which was to gain experience in that area, and ultimately of moving her closer to her vision of working with new mothers and babies in a community health agency.

If you want to take a lateral career direction, you need to find work that provides you with multi-skilling and cross-training opportunities. You may have to take the initiative and look for a lateral move, trade positions with a colleague in another area in the organization, or participate in an international exchange program. Often you may not be the one to initiate the lateral move. Some organizations routinely rotate staff laterally to keep them challenged and increase their employability skills. An organization may move you laterally because of restructuring or, because your current position became redundant, your union seniority may allow you to move laterally and "bump" another nurse. Regardless of the reason for the lateral move, always look upon it as a way to grow and increase your skills. In many situations your employer will provide continuing education to help you make the transition to the new position. Take advantage of the situation and build your repertoire of new skills.

Vertical — Moving Up

Even though fewer rungs are on the ladder today, opportunities will still arise to move up in an organization. Your evaluation of your strengths and limitations in your self-assessment may show that you have the ambition and ability to take on more responsibility. You may be one of those nurses who likes and wants the kind of job his or her manager has, wants more decision-making power, or just wants to feel that he or she is continually moving ahead. Begin your exploration of whether to take your career in a vertical direction by scanning your organization's internal environment and identifying both the organization's needs and your potential contribution. If you find congruence between them, then planning to take a vertical career direction may be very appropriate. For example Yael, the clinical nurse specialist in psychiatry described in the previous chapter, scanned her environment before she made a successful vertical move into an open managerial position at her hospital. This step also put her further on the road towards her career vision of becoming the manager of a psychiatric program at the regional level. The nurse manager whose ultimate vision was to become a CEO also moved vertically to achieve her short-term goal of obtaining a director of nursing position.

Occasionally individuals are promoted within an organization as a reward for excellence. But because of restructuring, in some cases positions that used to be perceived as representing a vertical move now actually constitute a lateral move. The position entails added responsibility but not added compensation. Some nurses take these positions because everyone thinks they should; who will do it if they don't? They accept the position, but then realize they made the wrong move. Be clear that such a move reflects your choice and that it fits with your career vision for yourself, not everyone else's career vision for you.

Realignment — Moving Down or Moving Out

Sometimes moving down may be the way to move forward. You may wish that you had a job with a more manageable schedule, and believe that time and flexibility are more important than increased responsibility. Taking on less responsibility could leave you with more time for family, school, volunteer work, or for pursuing your personal interests. The realignment career direction, or moving down, offers a way of increasing job satisfaction through decreased responsibility. It is an excellent choice to balance personal and professional goals. This option can include job sharing, part-time work, or a downward move in the organizational hierarchy. Take for example Caitlin, the nurse in the previous chapter who resigned from a full-time administrative position in a university nursing program. Moving in a realignment direction, from full- to part-time work and from an administrative to a teaching position, allowed her not only to spend more time with her family, but also to pursue her interest in teaching.

A few nurses may find that none of these three major career directions will lead them towards their career visions. Their interests have changed to such an extent that they want to leave the profession altogether. In their career visions they picture themselves, for instance, as running a bed and breakfast or working as a computer analyst. The career direction they choose, therefore, is moving out. If this is the path you decide will lead towards your goals, remember that regardless of your reasons for leaving nursing, you have many transferable skills that you can market successfully as you search for job opportunities outside the profession. Review your self-assessment to determine which of the numerous transferable skills you developed during your nursing career would make you most effective in other employment settings.

IDENTIFYING YOUR RESOURCES

The finest plans have always been spoiled by the littleness of them that should carry them out. Even emperors can't do it all by themselves.
Bertolt Brecht, *Mother Courage*

The most effective career plans usually are not developed in isolation. Having identified specific actions and career directions to take, you are now ready to look at the resources you may need to achieve your goal. The process of developing a plan requires you to think about who and what will help you implement your plan. Start by asking yourself the following questions:

Who should I talk to?
- Who do I know in a similar role?
- Who has been helpful as a mentor in the past?
- Who would I like to approach to be a mentor?
- Who do I want to meet?

What should I read?
- What resources are available to me now?
- Where can I look for information that I need to carry out the actions within my plan?
- How can I ensure that I keep up-to-date on what is going on in the world around me?

Where should I spend some time?
- What experiences will help me complete each action step?

What do I need to invest?
- How much time will each action step require?
- What financial commitment does my plan require?

For example, the nurse who envisioned working with children with special needs being cared for at home called on a variety of resources to implement the action steps he identified within his plan. In order to "spend time in the community with families of children with special needs," he talked to a neighbour about doing volunteer work in a day care setting for children with multiple handicaps. Through this activity, he was able to meet parents with first-hand experience of children's special needs and learned about gaps in the system. The nurse manager whose short-term goal was to develop advanced leadership skills planned the action step of completing an intensive executive leadership program. She identified that completing this course would require financial resources to cover travel, a leave of absence from work, child care arrangements, and the program fee. Knowing this in advance allowed her to plan for the necessary resources.

Making a thoughtful inventory of your available and potential resources is the first step you should take to begin to implement the action steps associated with each of your goals. Once you have determined the resources you will require, you will be ready to set timelines to accomplish your action steps.

SETTING TIMELINES

We all have examples of the "best plans" that never materialized into action. Successful career plans benefit from the rigour of specific timelines. Often, we hesitate to establish target dates for fear of not being able to meet them; yet, we all also have examples of plans where deadlines have helped us to accomplish the identified tasks. If your goal is personally motivating and your plan is realistic and concrete, assigning timelines simply ensures that you dedicate your resources in an efficient and ultimately rewarding way. Timelines should be suited to your particular needs and fit your personal priorities. For example, a nurse interested in pursuing doctoral studies determined first that in order to have access to the required financial resources, she would have to achieve this particular goal before her children were ready to enter university. Next, she assigned timelines to the individual activities associated with her goal.

Simpler activities also benefit from timelines. You can arrange for delivery of a daily paper, for example, but if you do not set aside some time to read it, your plan for keeping up with the world around you will remain simply a plan! Timelines can be modified, but including them at the outset is critical to developing an effective career plan.

ASSESSING AND RE-EVALUATING PLANS AND GOALS

Indicators of Success

How will you know that your plan is working? If you have documented your plan, including specific action steps, required resources, and timelines, you have a good start at identifying measures of success. Think about what you are hoping to accomplish with your plan. For example, completing a specific action step that clearly moves you towards a goal may be one indication of a workable plan. Assessing that you are professionally stimulated and happy doing what you are doing at a particular point in time may be another indicator of a successful career plan. Another sign of a good plan may be feeling that you have successfully taken charge of your own career. As you design your own plan, think about what success will look like for you. You also may define success differently at various stages in your career. Record your personal indicators to help you evaluate your plan at those different stages.

How Do I Keep My Plan Working for Me?

Career plans should be dynamic, responsive to personal circumstances, and professionally stimulating. In order to ensure that your plan remains flexible and relevant to your career vision, you must continuously re-evaluate your goals and your means of reaching them. You should be ready to adjust your plan as aspects of your self-assessment change, as your continuously updated environmental scan indicates that significant changes have occurred around you, or as you move into different stages of your career. Having a well developed strategic plan will also enable you to recognize and take advantage of career opportunities as they occur. For example, because the nurse who aspired to be a hospital CEO developed a detailed plan with concrete goals and action steps, she was able to seize opportunities for moving vertically towards her vision. As a series of circumstances arose, she advanced from a director of nursing position and from completing an executive leadership course to becoming president of a professional organization, a vice president of patient care, the chair of a provincial task force, and finally a CEO.

A nurse who thought he may like to work with the elderly had a short-term goal of finding a position that would let him "try it out." He accepted a casual position in a nursing home, which confirmed his interest in gerontology, gave him opportunities to gain experience and credibility as a practitioner, and eventually led to his being asked to consider a full-time position. Continual self-assessment helped this particular nurse to refine his plan and develop a concrete goal related to securing a full-time position working with the elderly.

The majority of nurses are involved in careers related to the provision of direct patient care. A nurse, for instance, whose career vision is to provide state of the art care for infants requiring neonatal nursing intervention used her career plan to ensure that she was constantly reviewing and adding goals to keep her plan working for her. After she worked 15 years in the same patient care unit, the hospital was closed. Having a plan served not only to keep this nurse current in her chosen area of practice, but it also made her marketable in a precarious job market. A community hospital recruited her to join a team of nurses being hired to open a level two nursery.

What Will You Do If You Lose Your Job Tomorrow? Do You Have a Plan?

Life is full of transitions – some natural such as growing older, some chosen such as going back to school, and others imposed such as job layoff. Today there are nurses who may have developed transition plans for returning to school, but may never have considered the need for developing a transition plan in the event that they lose their job tomorrow. In today's ever changing work environments, no one can be assured of a job for life. Some nurses will choose to leave their organizations for new opportunities. Others will be faced with the stark reality of receiving a layoff notice as the result of downsizing or restructuring.

Do you have a "what will I do if I lose my job tomorrow" plan? If not, the following are some questions you should think about as you start to develop your plan. Ask yourself, "What is the worst thing that could happen?" Don't wait until you receive a notice of layoff to answer. Anticipate possible scenarios and develop a plan for dealing with each of them. Being proactive will help you realize that you do have choices, even when it feels like you have none.

Support

We all benefit from having people around us to support us through various stages in our lives. Grieving is a natural part of job loss. Kubler-Ross (1969) identified five stages of grieving: denial, anger, bargaining, depression, and acceptance. Can you identify both a support group or person who could help you with the grieving process that occurs with job loss and others who will challenge you to stretch and move forward? Remember, your family can also be a significant support, but you need to keep them informed that a job loss is a very real possibility for you. Don't keep them in the dark.

You should also ascertain what supports your organization would provide. You may be eligible for outplacement counselling, career counselling, and employee assistance programs. You may also be eligible to participate in a government program that provides practical support specifically to health care workers who are laid off. Remember, this is the time to reach out and surround yourself with as much support as you need.

Financial situation

When we decide to make a major purchase, we generally assess our financial situation, then either go to our savings fund or begin to set aside the money. Developing a job transition plan requires that you go through a similar process. Have you recently done a thorough assessment of your financial situation? How much money do you need to live on monthly? How much money do you owe? Do you have an emergency fund put aside for a rainy day? Do you understand your employee benefits plan? If you had an option for early retirement, could you afford to take it? Do you know what the organization will provide in the way of financial support through its severance packages? Do you have a current copy of the Employment Standards Act or its equivalent from the responsible government agency that will define the minimum your employer must provide? Once you have the information you need, sit down with pen and paper. Itemize all your expenses and all your revenue sources, current and potential, and develop a financial plan to support you through the transition.

Leaving the organization

If you had a choice, how would you like to leave the organization? Would you prefer to leave with no formal acknowledgement other than the need for a friend to take you home? Or would you prefer to participate in some ritual, be that a farewell dinner or an afternoon tea? We all want and need to be acknowledged for our time and commitment to our jobs, but we all have very individual responses about how that should happen.

Do you have any idea of how the organization traditionally has given employees notice of layoff? How are its decisions communicated to others in the organization? How much notice is given? Do you have any choice over how you would like to be informed?

If you are part of a union, your collective agreement will outline guidelines about how the process will occur. If you are not part of a union, check your workplace human resource policy and procedures.

You should also consider getting the name of an employment relations lawyer who can provide direction and guidance throughout the process. Does your nursing association have a legal assistance program?

Taking care of yourself

In our workplaces and personal lives, we spend lots of time taking care of others. As you develop your job transition plan, build in components that focus on taking care of yourself. You need to give yourself some time to work things out after being laid off. You may want to consider joining a health club, participating in some relaxation sessions, or just taking some quality time for yourself to go away, do some self-reflection, and plan your next move. Also build some rewards for yourself into your plan that will celebrate successes along the way, such as time in your week for going for a walk, going to the movies, or meeting friends for coffee. How will you maintain your health, self-esteem, and relationships through the transition?

No matter how well you are prepared, receiving a layoff notice can be one of the most unsettling times in a career. Those who are proactive and take control of their lives more often than not think creatively and are solution focused. Start today by putting together a job transition plan that you can use if you lose your job tomorrow.

CONCLUSION

The more human beings proceed by plan the more effectively they may be hit by accident.
Friedrich Durrenmatt, *The Physicists*

Have you ever witnessed a colleague who appeared to "fall into" a particular career opportunity? Did you chalk it up merely to being at the right place at the right time? Yet experiences that appear to happen by accident often have their roots in a deliberate, clearly envisioned plan. Having a strategic plan helps you to take advantage of the "accidents" that are bound to occur. For instance, a nurse educator who was very determined that her interests and long-term career goals did not include management roles reluctantly agreed to assume a temporary position in a patient care manager role. At the end of the temporary assignment, she reported unexpectedly having had the opportunity to develop some of the skills that she identified as required in order to pursue her career vision. Without having a specific career plan, she may have viewed the management role as either an interference in achieving her own goals or as just a serendipitous experience. Instead, having a plan ensured that she turned what may have looked on the surface like an accidental experience into another step in her career journey. You, too, can make a career plan work for you. Whatever your career vision may be, having a plan will give you the advantage of recognizing accidents as opportunities and, ultimately, of taking control of a rewarding career.

REFERENCES

Donner, G., & Wheeler, M. (1993). *Taking control: Career planning for nurses*. Ottawa, Ontario: Canadian Nurses Association.

Kaye, B. (1993). *Up is not the only way: A guide to developing workforce talent*. Washington, DC: Career Systems.

Kubler-Ross, E. (1969). *On death and dying*. New York: Simon & Schuster.

FURTHER READING

Bridges, W. (1991). *Managing transitions: Making the most of change*. Reading, MA: Addison-Wesley.

Fox, D. (1996). Career insurance for today's world. *Training & Development, 50*(3), 61- 64.

Koonce, R. (1995). Becoming your own career coach. *Training & Development, 49*(1), 18-25.

Otte, F., & Kahnweiler, W. (1995). Long-range career planning during turbulent times. *Business Horizons, 38*(1), 2-6.

Stevens, P. (1992). Career planning for the individual. *International Journal of Career Management, 4*(1), 30-32.

Marketing Yourself, Your Skills, and Accomplishments

CHAPTER SIX

Using Self-Marketing Strategies to Achieve Your Career Goals

Lisa Pearlman, RN, MN

Lisa Pearlman is currently an Advanced Practice Nurse in the Heart Transplant Program at the Hospital for Sick Children where she specializes in assisting patients and families to manage the uncertainty of living with a life-threatening chronic illness. Lisa, who is active in several professional nursing organizations, has been an Associate of Donner & Wheeler since 1995.

In previous chapters, you have read about how the best preparation for the future is an investment in yourself. Through the process of self-assessment and self-discovery, you have asked yourself some very important questions to gain insight into who you are, how you fit amidst a constantly changing environment, and where you want to be in your career now and in the future. You have read about how essential it is to have a sound strategic career plan to transform your career possibilities into reality. But if you are like most people, you may also be experiencing some hesitation and feeling a little overwhelmed as you think about how you actually can begin to put that plan into motion.

A comprehensive self-marketing strategy is a vehicle that you can use to move from the planning to the action stage. Self-marketing enables you to take control of how you represent yourself to others. For nurses, self-marketing consists of making oneself visible, establishing a nursing network, forming a support group, finding a mentor, and creating targeted résumés, covering letters, and business cards. Self-marketing is a skill that must be learned. It takes time, effort, and determination. In this chapter, you will learn about the resources and tools that form the foundation of an effective self-marketing strategy that you can use to create your own opportunities and take control of your career and your future. Then in the chapter that follows, you will learn how to extend your self-marketing strategies through the interview process.

You: Your Best Marketer

When you conducted your self-assessment, you identified your values and beliefs and evaluated your past experience, accomplishments, strengths, and areas for improvement. Now that you have taken a close look at the things that make you unique, you can most effectively promote yourself by making yourself visible, maintaining your visibility, and using it to meet your goals. Your strengths, coupled with a commitment and belief in yourself, make you your own best marketer.

Each time you meet someone new or have the chance to speak to groups, you are presented with a marketing opportunity to accent your positives, take credit for your accomplishments, and remind others of how you are a contributor. To seize these opportunities effectively, you should rehearse a short self-promotional statement. Then when you meet people and are asked to talk about yourself, you will be ready to clearly and concisely articulate your knowledge, skills, and unique contributions with confidence and vision.

You do not need to wait for people to come to you. Making presentations to, and publishing for, both professional and community audiences are two strategies you can use to enhance your visibility. Consider writing articles for newsletters, newspapers, and professional journals. Become active in your professional association and interest groups and contribute to an initiative that will profile your talents and accomplishments.

Self-marketing also entails scanning the environment and "knowing your business." Having the ability to articulate who you are, what you want, and what you can do represents only half the equation. The other half is the ability to persuade others that what you have to offer meets the demands and challenges of the ever changing environment. Read newspapers, nursing and health care journals, annual reports, and anything else that will help you keep well informed about current and future trends. Become an expert in your field and demonstrate that you are a consumer of knowledge. Others cannot help but take their cues from you and respond positively.

Networking

Networking with others is a key component of successful self-marketing. The process of networking involves the development of mutually beneficial relationships through the exchange of personal and written resources (Brown, 1995; Hadley & Sheldon, 1995; Helfand, 1995). It is a way for people to connect and to build and maintain relationships so that they can help each other achieve their goals. Effective networking enables you to establish your presence, to create widespread visibility and exposure, to make others aware of your skills, talents, and accomplishments, and to gain access to the hidden job market (Brown, 1995; Lowstuter & Robertson, 1995; Prevost, 1995).

Networking can produce significant results if you believe in yourself and are committed and prepared to work at it. Remember, you are in control of finding the contacts you need to help you get what you want. The first step in developing your own network is to make a list of people you think may be helpful to you. Second, contact those people and be clear about what you are looking for and what you would like them to do for you. For the majority of nurses, networking begins in the workplace where there are innumerable opportunities to develop a professional network by leading or collaborating on work projects, sitting on committees, or participating in organizational workshops and conferences. Enrolling in university courses would also help you expand your professional network. The third step you could take is to target your network by attending conferences and seminars with the intention of meeting and speaking with others. Scan the environment to determine the current realities and future trends in the area that you are targeting. Finally, become extremely knowledgeable about the area in which you are interested so that you can engage in meaningful conversations and position yourself as being an expert (Hadley & Sheldon, 1995; Lowstuter & Robertson, 1995).

You can build your network by maintaining and tapping into ongoing alliances with friends, family, community contacts, classmates, colleagues, professors, and supervisors whom you have known over the years. Find out who knows whom, and speak to others who are presently doing or have done what it is you want to do. Keep in mind that it is not as important who you know as who knows you. When you meet with others, concentrate on who you are and what you can do for them.

Another excellent forum for networking is in the volunteer community. The people you meet during your volunteering will help expand your network. Your participation will also make you visible and perceived as a valuable contributor in the community. Moreover, volunteering serves as an opportunity to develop new skills and to gain experience and insight into a new environment.

Networking is the key to being and keeping "in the know" about what is going on in nursing and health care. It enables you not only to keep informed of current and emerging issues, but to develop a broad perspective about the constantly changing environment. As you have learned from previous chapters, once you know about the opportunities and barriers in the internal and external environment, you will be able to position yourself strategically and maintain your professional visibility.

Your network will also enable you to gain access to the hidden job market. It is common knowledge among those searching for employment that there are two job markets: formal and informal. The formal job market encompasses positions advertised in human resources departments, newspapers, and nursing and health care journals. But these positions account for only about 25% of the total number available at any given time (Brown, 1995; Hadley & Sheldon, 1995; Helfand, 1995).

With many nursing positions, employers fill openings through personal referrals or by hiring a nurse who happens to contact them at the right place at the right time. These practices not only save employers time and money by reducing advertising costs and targeting the selection process, but they enable them to invest in a nurse who is known and reputable. Therefore, if you are looking for a new position, plan to spend at least 75% of your time networking the informal or hidden job market (Brown, 1995; Hadley & Sheldon, 1995; Helfand, 1995).

Support Groups

Building and maintaining a support group is another valuable self-marketing strategy. Support groups are based on the principle that few people have ever accomplished what they want to solely on their own (Koonce, 1994; Sedlar & Miners, 1993). Your support group should consist of individuals who believe in you and want to see you succeed. Surround yourself with individuals who keep a positive attitude and are a source of confidence as you develop an action plan to reach your career goals. Seek out those whose feedback you value and whose emotional support you can count on, particularly when you take risks. Your circle of supporters can also provide you with instrumental support such as their computer expertise, proofreading abilities, child-care and transportation services, and company for social breaks (Haft, Heenehan, Taub, & Tullier, 1997).

Finding a Mentor

In addition to your network and support group, it is especially important to have a mentor to guide and support you as you plan to transform your dreams into reality. In the nursing community, mentors generally are experienced nurses who know the ins and outs of an organization, have more connections, and have more access to information than less experienced, often younger, nurses have. These experienced nurses, who already have made a significant contribution to nursing, are interested in sharing their knowledge and fostering leadership skills in less experienced nurses (Cooper, 1990; Madison, 1994).

By way of coaching and providing moral support, your mentor can help you scan the environment and give you feedback as you assess your own strengths, identify your career goals, and develop a career plan. Using his or her own network as a resource, your mentor may be able to enhance your professional visibility and socialization and provide you with career prospects (Madison, 1994). One nurse expressed her appreciation of her mentoring relationship and the high regard she had for her mentor's leadership, professional interests, and political savvy:

> She has always believed in me, ever since I was a new nurse 8 years ago. When I was a staff nurse in the hospital, she helped me to see new opportunities in the unit and consistently made herself available to discuss clinical and professional issues. When I left the hospital and became a public health nurse, we kept in touch, and she continues to be someone I still contact for guidance now and then. She always seems to know the "right thing to do." She helps me to see things from a broader perspective and I truly believe that from her, I have learned the value of leadership.

If you don't have a mentor, find one. Observe who in your nursing or professional community is well respected and possesses a leadership style that you admire. Select a mentor from whom you can learn the most and who may be interested in watching you grow professionally. Once you have identified a possible mentor, create both informal and formal opportunities for each of you to get to know one another. You can do this by volunteering to work on similar projects or by choosing to sit on a committee of which she or he is a member. If your prospective mentor does not work in the same organization, you may want to schedule an appointment to speak to her or him about your goals, what you have to offer, and what you are seeking from the mentoring relationship (Cooper, 1990; Madison, 1994). You may feel uncomfortable about approaching a potential mentor. But keep in mind that mentors also benefit from a relationship with a protégé. It helps them keep on top of the issues that nurses in general may be facing and also gives them the opportunity to contribute to the profession by developing nurses and helping them expand their networks.

STRATEGIES TO MARKET YOURSELF ON PAPER

The previous discussion has been focused on some of the "people resources" that are critical to self-marketing. What follows is an exploration of the "written resources" that complete a comprehensive self-marketing strategy: business cards, résumés, and covering letters.

Business Cards

In your current position, your employer already may have supplied you with a business card. However, one of the self-marketing strategies you should consider is also having a personal business card. When you network with key people, have your business card ready so that you do not fumble with a pen and paper.

Your business card represents you: make sure it does its job well (Hadley & Sheldon, 1995). It must be visually appealing and should include your name, credentials, address, telephone and fax numbers, and e-mail address. You can create the business card yourself on your computer or a print shop will design an attractive, inexpensive business card that can be ready within days. Before you place your order, ask to see the business cards of colleagues and friends to give you ideas about the design that would best reflect you.

Designing A Résumé That Works For You

A well-constructed résumé is your best written promotional piece. Like you, it is unique. An effective résumé will represent your knowledge, skills, and talents in such a convincing way that the reader can get an immediate sense of who you are and what you can do for them. Its primary purpose is to interest prospective employers enough in your qualifications to contact you for an interview.

Although many people assume that a résumé and curriculum vitae (CV) are the same thing, the two actually differ significantly. A résumé is a two to three page "snap-shot" of your career that is focused on your education, professional background, and accomplishments. A CV is a more detailed description of your professional and academic interests and accomplishments. It is usually over several pages long and reviews your lifetime career achievements. A CV generally is used to apply for grants, scholarships, awards, and academic appointments. A résumé, which is a focused summary of your achievements, is used to apply for a job (Hinck, 1997; Markey & Campbell, 1996). See Figure 6-1 for an outline of a curriculum vitae.

As with résumés, you must consider to whom you are sending the CV and for what purpose, and then customize your CV appropriately. Therefore, the order of the items as well as the selection of items will vary according to circumstances.

Types of résumés
There are three basic types of résumés: chronological, functional, and hybrid. Although no hard and fast rules apply about when to use each, some guidelines may help you decide which one is best suited to your circumstances.

The *chronological résumé* (see Figure 6-2) is the most traditional type of nursing résumé in which work history and education are described in reverse chronological order with the most recent experiences appearing first. Chronological résumés emphasize dates, position titles, responsibilities, and the names and locations of employing organizations. They work best for individuals who have

Figure 6-1: Outline for a Curriculum Vitae

1. **Name, Address, Phone/Fax/E-mail.**
2. **Education** – Degree granted, name, and location of institution.
3. **Academic Honours and Awards** – Name of award, name of award granting agency.
4. **Professional/Community Honours and Awards** – This category may be combined with no. 3.
5. **Current Position** – Position title, employing agency – if an academic position, follow this section with sections on undergraduate courses taught, graduate courses taught, and Masters or PhD students supervised.
6. **Previous Positions** – Position title, employing agency, brief description of role.
7. **Funded Research** – Grant name, granting agency, amount of grant.
8. **Publications** – Use a consistent and recognized format to list your publications, for example, the APA style. Use the following subsections: peer-reviewed, chapters in books, book reviews, and other publications.
9. **Academic Presentations** – These would include peer-reviewed abstracts or papers.
10. **Professional/Community Presentations** – These would include speeches and non-refereed papers.
11. **Peer Review Activities** – Grant reviews, journal reviews.
12. **University/Academic Boards and Committees** – Can be divided into university-wide and faculty or department categories.
13. **Professional Consultations** – Work you may have done for organizations, professional associations, etc.
14. **Professional Boards and Committees.**
15. **Community Service.**
16. **Special Appointments** – Any government or other appointments that you want to highlight separately.

Figure 6-2: Sample of a Chronological Résumé

Janet Black, RN, BScN
4905 Lorie Drive
Any City, Province P9T 5S8
Tel.: H: (986) 948-9037
W: (986) 816- 8645

Career Objective

To secure a staff nurse position in a palliative care environment that utilizes her expertise and 8 years of experience caring for oncology patients and their families.

EDUCATION

1989   **Bachelor of Science in Nursing**
                         Name of University
                         City, Province

HONOURS AND AWARDS

1996   Award of Excellence for Oncology Nursing, Metropolitan Hospital

EMPLOYMENT HISTORY

1995-Present   **Staff Nurse, Oncology Ambulatory Program**
                         Metropolitan Hospital, City, Province
                         Provides comprehensive nursing care to oncology patients receiving chemotherapy, which involves coordinating services between the inpatient unit, the outpatient setting, and the community.

                         Accomplishments: Is a hospital-wide resource for chemotherapy management; seconded to be a clinical resource nurse for the unit; initiated the "hospital to community" project; chosen to be a preceptor for baccalaureate students; frequently speaks to cancer support group.

1992-1995   **Staff Nurse Coordinator**
                         Provincial Cancer Health Centre, City, Province
                         In collaboration with the multidisciplinary team, coordinated services for cancer patients living at home.

Accomplishments: Revised the registry of community services for cancer patients; established links with organizations focusing on wellness and complementary therapies.

1989-1992   **Staff Nurse, Surgical Oncology Unit**
Metropolitan Hospital, City Province
Developed clinical expertise in oncology nursing, specifically the post-operative management of patients requiring surgical removal of malignancies.

Accomplishments: Certified to administer chemotherapy; presented inservices on "The impact of chemotherapy on body image"; rotated as the charge nurse.

COMMITTEE PARTICIPATION

1997-Present   Member, Provincial Oncology Group,
Metropolitan Health Centre
1996-Present   Secretary, Nursing Practice Committee,
Metropolitan Health Centre

PROFESSIONAL MEMBERSHIPS

Provincial Nurses Association
Canadian Nurses Association
Canadian Association of Nurses in Oncology
Staff Nurses Interest Group

PUBLICATIONS

Black, J. (1996). Facilitating early discharges for patients receiving chemotherapy. *Name of Journal, vol.,* pages.

CONTINUING EDUCATION

1997   Staff Nurse Leadership Certificate
Name of University, City, Province
1992-Present   Provincial Nursing Oncology Conference

COMMUNITY ACTIVITIES

1992-Present   Canadian Cancer Society, Local Chapter
Speakers Bureau

advanced their careers with positions of increased responsibility and/or preparation. Employers are most familiar with the chronological format and can easily scan the résumé to get what they need from it quickly (Haft et al., 1997; Markey & Campbell, 1996; Washington, 1996).

A *functional résumé* organizes work history according to functional themes. Individuals who have changed careers or jobs frequently, have large gaps in their employment history, or have not yet established a steady career path often choose a functional format. This format is particularly helpful in highlighting accomplishments rather than preparation and experience. Those nurses who wish to seek opportunities outside nursing or health care and want to profile their transferable skills may find the format most appropriate.

A *hybrid résumé* blends the strengths of both the chronological and functional formats (see Figure 6-3). It emphasizes career continuity as the chronological résumé does, while it also highlights the themes of expertise and accomplishments that appear in the functional format.

Résumé design

Since prospective employers often form their first impressions of you from your résumé, its presentation as well as its content can influence whether or not you are called for an interview. Your résumé must look business-like with an attractive layout, be easy to read, and present a moderate amount of white space. The best font sizes to use are 10 point and 12 point. Process your résumé through a laser printer using high-quality, light-coloured paper. Acceptable colours of résumé paper are ivory, natural white, or pale gray. Dark grays, browns, or bright colours are not visually appealing and are hard to read.

To ensure that your résumé is "dressed well," it should be on the same stock and colour paper as your covering letter. Stationery stores sell matching paper and envelopes that will enhance the impression your application makes upon a prospective employer. Once your résumé and covering letter are complete, staple the pages of the résumé together and use a paper clip to attach the résumé to your covering letter. If an employer asks you to fax your résumé, always forward the original hard copy. Facsimile copies are not as visually appealing as the original.

Figure 6-3: Sample of a Hybrid Résumé

Elizabeth Wilson, RN, BN
1234 Cobble Stone Drive
City, Province Postal Code
(H) Tel.: (456) 987-9045

Career Summary
Over 20 years of progressive leadership experience and demonstrated commitment in nursing administration. Superior skills in leading, facilitating, and coordinating large interdisciplinary groups to identify and meet strategic priorities. Recognized for exceptional ability to analyze and problem solve difficult and challenging situations. Instrumental in coordinating and implementing organizational redesign. An enlightened administrator who is committed to developing and maintaining collaborative working relationships within an interdisciplinary service model.

ACHIEVEMENTS

Corporate Leadership

Develops, implements, and evaluates creative and innovative solutions to manage programs through downsizing, restructuring, and re-engineering. Manages major policy development, program evaluation, and project implementation.
Demonstrates extensive knowledge in financial planning and forecasting, budgeting, and variance analysis.

Service Delivery

Leads business initiatives through the development of proposals.
Develops customer-specific programs.
Establishes liaisons with government agencies and private sector clients.

Quality Management

Possesses comprehensive knowledge of quality management design, implementation, and evaluation.
Establishes a framework and designs continuous improvement mechanisms that support strategic and operational goals.
Demonstrates leadership in directing the development of systems and processes to support outcome measurement and to optimize clinical efficiencies.

WORK EXPERIENCE

1990-Present   **Regional Director**
                     Community Health Care Organization, City, Province

                     Responsible for the overall business plan including admin-
                     istration and financial management; human resource
                     development; business development; service delivery;
                     community liaison; strategic and operational planning;
                     quality management; and education and research.

1983-1990   **Municipal Manager**
                     Community Health Care Organization, City, Province

                     Responsible for planning and organizing public health
                     unit's goals and objectives including staffing and man-
                     aging the budget.

1978-1983   **Staff Nurse, Municipal Public Health Branch**
                     Health Care Organization, City, Province

                     Coordinated well-baby clinics and post-partum home
                     visits.

EDUCATION

1997   Master of Nursing
                     Name of University
                     City, Province

1990   Baccalaureate in Nursing
                     Name of University
                     City, Province

1978   RN Diploma
                     Community College
                     City, Province

PUBLICATIONS

Wilson, E. (1995). Coping with organizational change. *Name of Journal, vol.,* pages.

COMMITTEE PARTICIPATION

1996   Chair, Nurses Week Committee
1995   Member, Strategic Planning Committee

PRESENTATIONS

Wilson, E. (date). *Name of presentation.* Name of organization. City, Province.

PROFESSIONAL MEMBERSHIPS

Provincial Nurses Association
Canadian Nurses Association
Canadian Public Health Association

COMMUNITY ACTIVITIES

1994   Chair, Fundraising Committee
              John Smith Public School

1990   Member, Board of Directors
              Barbara's Women's Shelter

Getting started

Creating a résumé can be a very intimidating experience, especially if you have not updated yours in years. It requires preparation, patience, and practice, practice, practice! The best time to write your résumé is when you do not need it. If you have been recently laid off or are under other pressures to meet an application deadline, such anxiety will interfere with your ability to create a dynamic winning product.

Remember, there is no such thing as a generic résumé. You need to target your résumé to ensure that it is effective for each specific opportunity you are pursuing. Many nurses who are beginning their job search enthusiastically send out their résumés in bulk hoping that they will be contacted by an employer. If the truth be known, this is a waste of time (Bolles, 1997). The effectiveness rate is minimal, and the time and money invested in merging covering letters and mailing résumés could be better used to scan the environment, develop a nursing network, personally contact employers, and set up meetings.

You need to customize your résumé for each position you are seeking. Use your résumé as a strategic marketing tool to accentuate the accomplishments, skills, and knowledge you identified as part of your self-assessment. Learn about the position and the organization, and scan the environment to determine what you can offer and how. What is the employer seeking? How do your knowledge, skills, and accomplishments relate to a particular position? What skills and experience can be transferable from your current or previous position to another position?

Does this mean that you may need to create more than one version of your résumé? The answer is yes! If, for example, you work as a staff nurse on a medical unit and are interested in making a lateral move to a critical care unit, your résumé should emphasize your diverse and in-depth clinical knowledge, your ability to manage acute, urgent patient problems, your flexibility, your organization skills, and your commitment and dedication to providing patient-focused care.

To help you understand what employers are looking for, scan the employment advertisements in journals and newspapers for similar positions. In the following example, the employer is looking for a front-line nurse manager for a moderate-sized community hospital:

Requires a high energy, innovative person to provide leadership and direction amidst constant change and adversity. As the Nursing Unit Manager of Emergency, you will manage a multidisciplinary staff to ensure an integrated approach to patient care. You possess a minimum of 5 years of nursing practice with at least 3 years in management. Proven leadership, team building, and problem-solving skills are requirements complemented by current knowledge of new concepts and trends in emergency room nursing.

What does this advertisement say to you? It calls for a nurse who is an innovative leader, who demonstrates exemplary nursing practice, and who manifests strong abilities to think critically, manage change, and collaborate with others. When you respond to similar advertisements or position descriptions, be sure to customize your résumé by using specific examples and concrete outcomes from your own experiences in order to convey the message that you possess exactly what the employer is seeking.

In the next example, a Women's and Children's Health Unit is advertising for a staff nurse to work in its community birthing centre:

The successful candidate must have 3-5 years of progressive experience in women's and children's health providing counselling and support to labouring women and their families, and must possess strong team leadership and communication skills, strong resource management abilities, and excellent program development and evaluation skills.

If you are a nurse who fits this description, you need to convey that in your résumé. Refer to your self-assessment and reality check and identify concrete examples of your leadership in maternal-child nursing. Answer the following questions: What is unique about the way you provide support to labouring women? How have you advanced the practice in women's and children's health? What feedback have you received about your role as a team player? How has your leadership benefited your patients and their families as well as the staff in the unit where you work?

Anatomy of a résumé

As a strategic marketing tool, your résumé should begin with a *career objective* or a *career summary*. A career objective is a statement of what you are looking for that is focused, although not so restrictive as to limit your employment options (Haft et al., 1997). Newly graduated nurses frequently use a career objective to indicate to a prospective employer what type of position they are seeking. Figure 6-2 provides an example of a résumé with a career objective.

A career summary affords you the opportunity to make a strong, positive impression "up front," by summarizing your strengths, accomplishments, expertise, and career interests. It works best for nurses who have more than 10 years of work experience. Many of the talents and accomplishments that you highlighted in your self-assessment can be emphasized here. The advantage of a career summary is that it serves to whet the appetite of prospective employers and intrigue them to move on to the rest of the résumé (Haft et al., 1997). Figure 6-3 provides an example of a résumé with an effective career summary.

Many nurses highlight their *education* in separate formal academic and continuing education categories, whereas others combine the two into one section. Whichever strategy you choose, remember that you want to emphasize your commitment to continuous learning and professional development. Present your academic education in reverse chronological order. In a chronological résumé, your education is most often listed directly after your career objective or career summary and before your work experience on the first page. This allows the employer to determine quickly that you have the minimal educational requirement. In a hybrid résumé, education is usually listed on the second page, whereas in a functional résumé, it may not be listed at all.

If you choose to list your *continuing education* as a separate category, do so but position it further down (see Figure 6-2). Include only those conferences and workshops relevant to your professional growth and career development and to the position for which you are applying. If you have attended several continuing education offerings, you have the option of writing "selected" beside this category, which enables you to further customize your résumé.

If you have received *honours and awards* from your workplace, academic institution, or professional nursing association, highlight them in a separate category to accentuate their merit. Remember to state the year you received your honours and awards and the names of the sponsoring organizations (Markey & Campbell, 1996; Weinberg, 1994).

Your professional *work experience* forms the main body of a chronological résumé. Nurses use a variety of terms to describe this section: *employment history, professional background, work history, employment experience, or professional experience.* Whichever term you choose, remember that the intent of this section is to demonstrate your career progression by describing your ongoing contributions and accomplishments (Washington, 1996). Examine your self-assessment and focus on your knowledge, skills, talents, and accomplishments. What was unique about them? How did they change things in your work environment? Be specific about the outcomes that occurred as a result of your accomplishments. Such accomplishments, which separate achievers from non-achievers, will reflect excellence in your practice and indicate how you manage responsibility.

Kathy, for example, has filled various nursing education roles in a rehabilitation setting for the past 10 years. Her overall responsibility is to provide clinical support and education to the nurses in three patient care areas. In her self-assessment, Kathy was able to expound upon her responsibilities by describing her accomplishments. On her résumé, Kathy gave several specific examples of her abilities (a) to integrate nursing research into practice; (b) to develop, implement, and evaluate a hospital-wide professional development plan; and (c) to liaise with community hospitals in developing standards for caring for a specialized patient population.

In a functional résumé, however, you would focus more on your major skills and accomplishments than on outlining your work experience. Most people choose between two and four functional headings that are customized to match a specific position. In a hybrid résumé, you would illustrate your work experience both with functional themes and an employment history. For example, Elizabeth Wilson (see Figure 6-3) highlighted the functional themes of corporate leadership, service delivery, and quality management in addition to supplying a chronological work history in her résumé.

On your résumé, list only your current *professional memberships and affiliations*, including any office you may have held. This demonstrates that you are keeping up-to-date with your profession and that you have developed useful contacts (Washington, 1996). Since more

Canadian nurses are becoming certified in their clinical specialties, you should list any *professional certification* you have, including the certification body. This is an important marketing strategy, particularly if you are applying for a position where a specific certification is a requisite qualification.

By listing your *professional publications and presentations* on your résumé, you demonstrate your expertise and knowledge in your particular area as well as your ability to engage in research and scholarly writing. If you have written health education manuals, client-teaching tools or published a professionally related article in a popular journal, definitely include them in this section. If you have numerous publications and/or presentations, customize your résumé by indicating that only selected ones are listed. This strategy provides the employer with insight into your skills and provides you with flexibility to control the length of your résumé. Be sure to include co-authors in this section. Remember that as a member of a research team, even if as a data collector, you are entitled to be cited as a contributor on any publication. Make sure to negotiate this when you are recruited.

List your most recent *community-related volunteer activities*, including the dates and names of the organizations. Provide details about your volunteer work if you believe that they will further customize your résumé. You may add *References on Request* at the end of your résumé; however, it is more appropriate to have them available when requested. Chapter Seven will include a more detailed discussion of the most effective approach to references.

Résumé Do's
- Aim for two to three pages.
- Create your résumé to be accomplishments and results focused.
- Customize your résumé for each position you seek.
- Eliminate any redundant information.
- Include a career objective or career summary at the top of the first page of your résumé.
- Ensure that you use proper spelling and grammar.
- If the employer requests a faxed copy of your résumé, send the original copy through the mail.

Résumé Don'ts
- Do not enclose a photo.
- Do not include your birth date, nationality, religious, or political affiliations.
- Do not mention salary.
- Do not repeat your job description.
- Do not send a résumé without a covering letter.
- Do not send a résumé on your current institution's letterhead.
- Do not attach reference letters to your résumé.
- Do not send your résumé indiscriminately.

Your Covering Letter

Your résumé should always be accompanied by a one-page covering letter. The purpose of a covering letter is to encourage prospective employers to read your résumé more carefully to determine how your experience and abilities can benefit their organization. It should be written on personal letterhead and attached with your personal business card, which together give the readers all the details they need to get in touch with you.

Every word, phrase, and sentence in your covering letter must demonstrate how your qualifications match what the employer is seeking. If you don't have *all* the qualifications (and most applicants don't!), explain why you believe that your knowledge, skills, and accomplishments would make you successful in the position. Remember to write your covering letter after you have completed your résumé so that you can emphasize and expand on matching your skills and abilities with the employer's specific requirements.

A covering letter has three main components. Your opening statement should outline the position you are applying for and where you found out about the opportunity (see Figure 6-4). This introduction will quickly engage the reader's interest. The second component, which is the main body, should emphasize why you are interested in the position and what you have to offer. It should also mention that the enclosed résumé will provide more supporting details about your qualifications. Remember, the goal of your covering letter is to convince prospective employers that they will benefit if they decide to

Figure 6-4: Sample of a Covering Letter

4905 Lorie Drive
Any City, Province
P9T 5S8
Tel.: (986) 948-9037

Date

Ms. Kathleen Drake
Program Director
Palliative Care Program
Metropolitan Health Centre
Any City, Province P2L 2L5

Dear Ms. Drake:

I am writing in response to the advertisement posted on the Human Resources Bulletin Board for the Staff Nurse position in the Palliative Care Program.

As a staff nurse working in the oncology unit, I am excited about the opportunities that a new palliative care program would provide for patients and staff. In my career here at Metropolitan, I have developed clinical expertise and in-depth knowledge in caring for oncology patients. I have also spearheaded several initiatives with community agencies to facilitate early discharge, which has heightened my awareness of the need for a palliative care program in our hospital. My enclosed résumé gives more details about my qualifications, skills, and accomplishments.

I would be delighted to discuss my potential contribution to this new initiative and look forward to hearing from you.

Yours truly,

Janet Black, RN, BScN

find out more about how you can meet their needs. Rely on your skills inventory and your understanding of the environment to match your skills, abilities, and accomplishments with the needs and interests of the employer. The letter's last component is a closing paragraph in which you then request an interview to discuss the possible fit between what the employer is looking for and what you have to offer (Haft et al., 1997; Koonce, 1994; Washington, 1996).

FINAL THOUGHTS

Self-marketing is about using all your resources to present yourself in the strongest, most positive way. Remember that the foremost resource you have to shape your own future is you! But your network, support group, and mentor also all play key roles in helping you to understand the environment, to take inventory of your personal and professional self, and to assist you to reach your career goals. Effective résumés, covering letters, and business cards can be the most successful means of promoting yourself on paper and making lasting impressions. Keep your goal in mind. Creating an effective self-marketing strategy that works for you takes time, effort, and patience. Following these strategies will contribute to realizing your goals.

REFERENCES

Bolles, R. N. (1997). *The 1997 what color is your parachute? A practical manual for job-hunters & career changers*. Berkeley, CA: Ten Speed Press.

Brown, M. (1995). *Landing on your feet: An inspirational guide to surviving, coping and prospering from job loss* (2nd ed.). Toronto: McGraw-Hill Ryerson.

Cooper, M. D. (1990). Mentorship: The key to the future of professionalism in nursing. *Journal of Perinatal and Neonatal Nursing*, 4(3), 71-77.

Hadley, J., & Sheldon, B. (1995). *The smart woman's guide to networking*. Franklin Lake, NJ: Career Press.

Haft, T., Heenehan, M., Taub, M., & Tullier, M. (1997). *Job smart*. New York: Random House.

Helfand, D. P. (1995). *Career change: Everything you need to know to meet new challenges and take control of your career.* Lincolnwood, IL: VGM Career Horizons.

Hinck, S. M. (1997). A curriculum vitae that gives you a competitive edge. *Clinical Nurse Specialist, 11,* 174-177.

Koonce, R. (1994). *Career power.* Toronto, Ontario: Amacom.

Lowstuter, C. C., & Robertson, D. P. (1995). *Network your way to your next job…fast.* Toronto, Ontario: McGraw-Hill.

Madison, J. (1994). The value of mentoring in nursing leadership: A descriptive study. *Nursing Forum, 2*(4), 16-23.

Markey, B. T., & Campbell, R. L. (1996). A résumé or curriculum vitae for success. *Association of Operating Room Nurses Journal, 63,* 192-202.

Prevost, S. S. (1995). Maintaining your marketability in changing times. *Clinical Nurse Specialist, 9*(2), 67,74.

Sedlar, J., & Miners, R. (1993). *On target: Enhance your life and ensure your success.* New York: MasterMedia.

Washington, T. (1996). *Résumé power: Selling yourself on paper.* Bellevue, WA: Mount Vernon Press.

Weinberg, J. (1994). *How to win the job you really want* (2nd ed.). New York: Henry Holt.

FURTHER READING

Gonyea, J., & Gonyea, W. (1996). *Electronic résumés: A complete guide to putting your résumé on line.* New York: McGraw Hill.

Swartz, M. (1997). *Get wired, you're hired.* Scarborough, Ontario. Prentice Hall Canada.

Tallier, M. (1997). *Networking for everyone.* Indianapolis, IN: JIST Works.

Wickman, F., & Sjodin, T. (1997). *Mentoring: A success guide for mentors and protégés.* Chicago: Irwin.

CHAPTER SEVEN

The Interview: An Excellent
Self-Marketing Opportunity

Lorna Hegarty, BSc and Mary Wheeler, RN, MEd

Lorna Hegarty has worked in the field of human resources for the past 18 years. She has a special interest in career planning and job search skills, and is the President of INTERprep Inc., a company dedicated to assisting individuals with job search and career planning.

I n previous chapters you learned about self-marketing and how to rely on various human and written resources to promote yourself. The interview is another excellent self-marketing opportunity that you will have many occasions to use over the course of your career. Whether you are interviewed for a job, for school, or for a volunteer position, you will need finely honed interviewing skills. In this chapter, you will learn how to develop those skills in the context of the job-seeking process. But they are strategies that you can also transfer successfully to a wide variety of other interview situations.

For many nurses the idea of having to go to a job interview can be paralyzing, whether the advertised position is inside or outside their current organization. Most nurses have been in the same position for a long time and actually may never have participated in a job interview. Not so long ago situations arose when the only interview question for an interviewed job was, "Can you start today?" But lately the interview process has become complex and time consuming; sometimes applicants must participate in two to three interviews before a final decision is made.

Remember that the interview, a self-marketing opportunity for both the potential employer and the employee, really is a two-way exchange of information. It give employers an opportunity to market their organization and their department or unit to you while they also decide whether you will be a good fit within their organization. At the same time, the interview gives you the chance to market yourself to the prospective employer by demonstrating in your answers to the interview questions that not only do you have the ability to do the job, but you are also the best candidate to meet the employer's needs. This strategy will require you to promote yourself, not an easy prospect for many nurses. The interview also gives you an opportunity to have your questions answered so that, if you are offered the position, you will be able to make a well informed decision about whether the position is the right one for you.

The purposes of this chapter are to look in detail at the three distinct steps in the interview process, *preparation, the actual interview*, and *follow-up*, and to provide you with some valuable strategies you can use to get the job you want. In step one, preparation, you need to review your accomplishments, consider what the employer is looking for, and think about how to make the connection between the two. You will then have the tools to persuade the employer that you can fulfil the requirements of the position. Your task in step two, the interview, is to demonstrate that what you can offer is what they need. In step three, the follow-up, you evaluate your performance and weigh the pros and cons of the position so that you will be prepared if you are offered the position.

STEP ONE: PREPARATION

Once you get the phone call to come for an interview, say to yourself, "I have some skill or talent that they need. If I didn't, they would not have called me." This attitude will help you move through the interview process with confidence. Before you hang up the phone, find out when and where the interview will be and the name of the contact person. Now you are ready to move into the interview process.

The better prepared you are before the interview begins, the easier it will be during it to focus on promoting yourself as being the right person for the position. That means that before you go, you should have completed a comprehensive self-assessment, be clear about your options, and have set realistic goals. If you have done your homework, researched the organization to understand its mandate and goals, and contemplated the fit with your own goals, you'll do well. This preparatory step is also when you review and practice common interview questions you may be asked, formulate interview question strategies, prepare questions you may want to ask the interviewer, and notify your references about your upcoming opportunity.

Research

Before you submitted your résumé, you did some fairly extensive research about facets of the organization. Now that you have been called for an interview, you need to fill in the gaps. All employers prefer a well prepared candidate who has made an effort to learn about their organization, department, or unit. As well, you can make a more informed decision about whether to take a position if you know as much as possible about the organization and what its plans are for the future. You can obtain this information through your network, the organization's Communications or Public Affairs Department, or from pamphlets, newsletters, or brochures which the organization may have prepared for the community and which may be available in your local library. If possible, visit the organization before the interview, and see what information they make available in public areas for staff and others. Monitor the newspapers to keep informed of events that signal growth or change to a particular organization, for instance, a new source of funding or changed legislation. This strategy will not be new to you because you already know the importance of continuously scanning the environment.

Next do some research about the position. Get a copy of the job description from the contact person whose name you received when you were called about the interview. Also ask for the organization's most recent and relevant publication, for example, its Annual Report or Strategic Plan. These documents may indicate the longer term potential of the position within the organization. For example, if you have applied for a position in labour and delivery and you find out that the unit will be closing within 4 months, you may want to reconsider your application. Or you may want to ask more questions.

Although the unit is scheduled to close, the organization may be planning to move into community prenatal education and parental support. As you know from your self-assessment, these are also areas in which you have the skills to work. Other research questions may include, "What is the salary range?" and "Is it a unionized position?"

Try to find out about the interview itself. Who will be interviewing you? What will be the stages? Will there be a single interview only or will it be part of a serial interview? Will the interview be conducted one-on-one or with a panel? Will any tests be administered? How long is the interview expected to last – an hour, half a day? Depending on the position, you may be asked to do anything from developing a strategic plan to designing an organizational chart. That is why you want as much information as possible; you don't want to be surprised. Also determine how long it will take to get to the interview. If you are not familiar with the site, take a dry run so that you will not get lost on the day of the interview.

Preparing Yourself

Most interviewers would agree that they are looking for the following when they interview candidates: clinical and technical competency, strong communication and interpersonal skills, flexibility, and commitment to the position. Other attributes of interest would be the abilities to manage stress, juggle multiple tasks, and generally be well organized, as well as to be a good problem solver, risk taker, and critical thinker. The preparation step is the time to create a positive feeling about yourself and your potential and to clarify how your skills fit with the job requirements and the employer's values and culture.

Your preparation should include both an honest assessment of your strengths and limitations in the context of the position you have applied for and a review of potential interview questions and how best to answer them. Refer back to Chapter Three about self-assessment. As part of that process, you had to identify your accomplishments as well as your skills. Then in Chapter Six, you were introduced to the concept that a résumé is a record of your accomplishments. Now compile a list of your personal attributes, skills, and accomplishments which is based on your self-assessment and résumé. What qualities do you see? What qualities do you think the organization saw? What do you think caught their eye on your résumé, and what do you think they want to know more about? Whatever it is, it will be the value added, your potential unique contribution to their organization. Can you match your professional experience to the skills, abilities, and knowledge essential for the position? Can you cite specific situations that would demonstrate each match?

Based on the position, consider whom you may use as a reference, those who know you and the unique skills you are going to market in the interview. You need to be strategic as you consider possible references. Now is the time to develop a list of individuals who can be called upon later. You may want to alert them that you are in the job search market.

Questions, Questions, Questions

The preparation step is the time to develop a list of the questions you think the employer will have for you and the ones that you will have for them. The key to a successful interview is knowing how to listen to the questions and how to answer them appropriately. If it has been a long while since you participated in an interview, you will find the following review of categories and types of questions helpful. Each type of question is asked for different purposes and each requires a different response. Understanding why these questions are asked will help you formulate effective approaches to use to ensure that your interview is successful.

In general, there are two basic categories of interview questions: closed and open (Trefiak & Volpe, 1990). Closed questions, which interviewers use to inventory specific skills, can be answered either "yes" or "no" with little or no elaboration. These questions could include whether you have worked with a budget or are familiar with, or have practised, specific clinical procedures. Open questions, which cannot be answered with a simple yes or no, are used to elicit detailed, usually revealing responses. A question frequently asked at the very beginning of interviews is, "Tell me about yourself" or "Tell us why you would like to work here in this position." The best response is a succinct accounting of your professional history and accomplishments and how they fit the position requirements and the organization's vision.

Within both open and closed question categories, there is a further range of different types of interview questions (Trefiak & Volpe, 1990). Factual questions allow you to help the interviewer understand some of the details about you and your past experience. For example, "Where did you take your gerontology course?" Technical questions relate to the skills required to do the job, for example, your specific clinical skills and knowledge, your administrative knowledge, or your teaching philosophy. Situational questions usually follow a hypothetical situation or case study that the interviewer poses. The situations would be typical of what may arise in the kind of position for which you are applying. These questions are asked to evaluate how you would problem solve in different situations. For example, "How would you respond to the patient in this situation?," "How would you resolve the conflict between those team members?," or "How do you deal with the student in that situation?" may help the interviewer determine your prospective behaviour in such situations. Interviewers may ask these questions in many ways. They may use probing, leading, or confirming questions. These questions and styles should be familiar to you. During your nursing education and as part of your continuing practice, you have adopted many of the same techniques used in these questions to communicate with clients and colleagues.

What follows is a list of more specific questions from all the categories and types you may encounter and ones for which you should have prepared some answers. Think about how you would answer them. Develop some situations and examples that you can use to demonstrate why you would be the best candidate for the position:

1. Tell us about yourself, your background, education, and career history.
2. Describe your present job; what do you like and not like about it?
3. Where do you see yourself in 5 years? What are your long-term career goals?
4. What motivates you? What do you have a passion for in nursing?
5. What words describe you best? What words would others use to describe you?
6. Describe a work situation that you feel very proud about and why.
7. What is the most difficult work situation you have had to deal with and how did you handle it?

8. What are your strengths? What are your weaknesses?
9. Why do you want to work for this organization? Why do you want this job?
10. Why should we hire you? How can you make a difference in this organization?

The interviewer should provide you with many opportunities to talk about your strengths and accomplishments. As you prepare your responses, keep your accomplishments in mind. Most interviewers also want to know about the challenges you have faced, the approaches you used to deal with them, the results you achieved, and how you made a difference. If as is common, you are asked about your weaknesses, practise turning this question around to your advantage. Rather than listing your weaknesses, consider demonstrating your ability to learn from experience. For example, describe what you learned from a particularly difficult situation and how you would handle it next time.

Practise responding to questions in front of a mirror or with a friend, colleague, or family member so that you can identify and work on avoiding common interview mistakes (like fidgeting, avoiding eye contact, or rambling when asked a specific question). As you prepare for the interview, put yourself in the interviewer's shoes. What qualities or attributes do you think would appeal to him or her? Try to think of qualities in the context of the job for which you are being interviewed.

Once you have reviewed and practised some of the questions you may be asked, you should develop a list of questions you need answered in the interview to help you in your decision-making process. Remember that the questions you ask during the interview indicate your priorities and interests. For instance, even though salary and benefits may be your priority, detailed questions about them generally are not appropriate until you have been offered the position. A positive, proactive attitude would more likely be construed if you were to ask any of the following questions. But don't limit your questions. Let these function as a springboard to others that may be more relevant to you and your situation:

1. What are the organization's/department's/unit's philosophy and goals?
2. What are the key responsibilities of this position?
3. What do you think the challenges of this job will be?

4. Can you describe the culture of this organization/department/unit?
5. What is your management style like? To whom would I report?
6. What would be your expectations of me as a member of your staff?
7. Why do you like working here?
8. What are the opportunities for development?
9. What are the next steps in the process? Will you be holding second interviews? When will the hiring decision be made? (These are good closing questions because they may lead to a discussion about your viability as a candidate and your chances of being hired.)

As you complete step one in the interview process, you should feel confident that your extensive research has helped you understand the needs of both the organization and the department or unit. After developing your questions and practising them by yourself and with a colleague, you should be able to convincingly articulate why you have the skills, talents, and attributes that the organization wants and the position requires. Finally, on reflection you should be clear about how and why this position will meet or further your own career goals. Now you are ready for the interview.

STEP TWO: THE INTERVIEW

During the interview you want to be at ease and be able to concentrate so that you can listen to the questions and answer them wisely. To do this you need to be well organized and physically and emotionally ready. The interview itself can be stressful so you don't want other stressful elements to intrude on the day. The following are some strategies and tips that will decrease your anxiety and help you feel prepared. Plan to arrive 10 to 15 minutes before the interview is to start. Select clothing that helps you to feel comfortable yet professional. Be sure that it has been cleaned and pressed and that you have the appropriate accessories. Prepare your briefcase or portfolio with an extra copy of your résumé, your list of questions, and a list of your references just in case you are required to give them to the interviewer.

Once you reach your destination, check in with the receptionist or front desk and let them know you have arrived. Know your interviewer's name. If you are offered a coffee and would like to have one, go ahead. If you think you need water in the interview, ask for it. If your interviewer is running late, don't complain to the receptionist and don't leave. Be aware that the receptionist may be asked about the behaviour of candidates in the waiting area. While waiting for your interview, use the time to review the job description, your résumé, and your questions. If you feel nervous, try to relax by breathing in deeply as you silently count to six and visualize yourself in the position for which you are being interviewed. Hold your breath and silently count to six, then exhale. Repeat the process five or six times. Now you are ready for the interview. It usually consists of three stages: breaking the ice, the "real interview" and information gathering, and closing the interview.

Breaking The Ice

Your initial opportunity to make a good impression begins as soon as you are invited into the room for the interview. When your greet the interviewer, smile, look directly into his or her eyes, and shake hands firmly. If there are others in the room, make either hand or eye contact with them. Once you have finished the greeting, concentrate on appearing pleasant and relaxed. Maintain eye contact. Choose your seat wisely. If there is a swivel chair, ask for a chair that won't move about. Breaking the ice is when such topics as the weather or traffic are discussed. Be alert to a change in body language or a brief silence that signals that the real interview is about to begin. Be conscious of your own body language; sit in the "success" posture: feet on the floor, shoulders back, and lean in slightly towards the interviewer.

The Real Interview

In step one, preparation, you reviewed questions you possibly would be asked and prepared appropriate answers. When finally at the interview, don't jump into answering a question with your prepared response. Take your time to think over each question and formulate good answers. Be succinct and use examples whenever possible (since actions speak louder than words). Focus on your strengths as much as you can, and monitor your progress by watching the interviewer's body language. If you find that the interviewer is looking away from you or repeatedly checking his or her watch, there is a good chance that your answers are too long and detailed. Shortening your answers or speeding up your delivery, may be all that is required to regain the interviewer's attention and interest in you as a candidate.

Focus on the interviewer's entire question. You may assume that you know what the interviewer is going to ask and rush to formulate an answer. If you have misjudged, you may miss the second half of a question or, worse yet, interrupt the interviewer in mid-sentence. Allow the interviewer to set the tone and pace of the interview. Answer only direct questions. Be honest in your answers, and be friendly and enthusiastic. When asked, share your goals and aspirations. Avoid repeating yourself, and speak only of relevant experience. In your responses demonstrate knowledge of the organization. Most important, have a positive attitude. Believe that you can answer the interviewer's questions with confidence. Listen carefully, and if you are not sure you understand, ask that the question be repeated. If you don't know the answer, say so. If a question is asked and, for the moment, you go blank but want to respond, let the interviewer know that you would like to think about it and come back to it in a couple of minutes.

Even though salary generally is discussed only when a position has been offered, some interviewers may ask you what your salary expectations are. You can approach this question in several ways. You may ask them if they are offering you the position and, if so, you would be pleased to discuss salary. Or you may choose to let them know you would be pleased to discuss salary when they offer the position. But if you think it appropriate and want to discuss salary, use the information you collected in your preparatory research about salary ranges for the position in this and other organizations. Talk about range of salary rather than limiting yourself to an amount which may be higher or lower than the position pays.

Be reminded that human rights codes across Canada prohibit discrimination in employment on various grounds. Questions that contravene human rights legislation include inquiries about race, religion, age, and marital status. If asked, you may respond by saying something like, "I understand these questions are prohibited by legislation." But try to respond in a straightforward, non-aggressive manner.

Once the interviewers have asked their questions, you have your opportunity to ask yours. Refer back to the questions you developed when you prepared for the interview. Some interviewers are very thorough in their descriptions of the position and their expectations. If that is the case and you have no questions, don't dream something up. Thank the interviewers for their time and let them know that all your questions have been answered.

Not only is the interview an opportunity for you to get your questions answered, but it also gives you a chance to observe the people with whom you will be working and their group dynamics. The way they communicate both with you and among themselves is a good indicator of what it would be like working beside them day by day. Therefore, as they are deciding whether you will fit with them, you should be doing the same.

Closing The Interview

Body language will change again as the interviewers bring closure to the interview. Once both sides have asked and had their questions answered, the final piece of information often is, "What will be the next step?" After that is asked, thank the interviewers and shake their hands as you prepare to leave.

Although the focus here has been on you as an interviewee, you also may have many opportunities to be an interviewer, either as a part of a team, as a manager, or as a member of an admissions committee in a school of nursing. The process and questions that have been described are also ones you can use to help you develop your interviewer skills for those occasions.

STEP THREE: FOLLOW-UP

Well you made it through the interview. How did it feel? In step three, follow-up, as you wait for the phone call, you should evaluate your performance. Review the interview and determine what you learned, what you would change the next time, and make notes. If possible, review the interview with a colleague for both support and constructive feedback.

Some people send a thank you note after the interview. This custom is optional and clearly based on personal style. Even if you are not interested in the position, you can still express appreciation for being considered. Thank you notes can be a valuable networking tool, whether for the current position for which you applied or to keep you in the interviewer's mind for positions that may appear in the future.

If you have not heard from the interviewer within the time frame identified, wait a few more days. Then call and ask where they are in the hiring process and whether a decision has been made. In many organizations new priorities surface every day, and hiring decisions may be moved down the list of priorities. Don't despair: get clarification about the new time frame.

Your References

Reference checks usually are conducted only for candidates whom the interviewer has identified as the leading contender for the position. In step one, preparation, you identified and contacted individuals who were willing to be a reference for you. When selecting individuals to act as your reference, you should have come up with a minimum of three people whom you either worked for or worked with in the last 5 years. When asked to provide a reference from someone you have worked for, you do not necessarily have to offer your current manager's name. Choose someone you worked for who will provide you with an excellent reference. If you do not have that kind of relationship with your current manager or with anyone else on your list of references, then do not use them. After considering the interview and the position, offer the interviewer references who will enhance the information you provided in the interview. Never give the name of an individual whom you have not contacted beforehand and whose permission you have not secured. Contact your references personally to alert them that they may get a phone call. Let them know the position for which you were interviewed, discuss the interview with them, and review what you would like them to say about you. You want them to have as much information as possible so that they can speak knowledgeably about you and give you the best reference possible. Generally the interviewer will phone references and ask them open-ended and probing questions to get a realistic assessment of you.

The Job Offer

Congratulations! Your references were checked, and you got the job offer. Now you need to evaluate the job and the offer and then make a decision. Allow yourself adequate time to do this. If you receive a verbal offer, it is a good idea to get confirmation of the job responsibilities, salary, and benefits in writing. You may be asked to sign a letter in which you formally accept the job, and usually within 24 to 48 hours, so you have time to review the pros and cons of the offer. If you are uncertain about whether to accept the job, create a "for" and "against" list. Putting your thoughts on paper will help you make an informed decision. This may also be the time to look back at your self-assessment and career vision and see how closely the position would fit in. You can also use your mentor to help with the decision making. If the "for" list outweighs the "against," and the job meets your career planning objectives, then acceptance is worth considering. If it is the other way around, then trust your judgment; do not be tempted to take a job if you have nagging doubts.

If there are some aspects of the job offer that you would like to negotiate, such as the job expectations or compensation, now is the time. Most negotiations centre around compensation. If the position is unionized, then salary and benefits have already been negotiated on your behalf by the union. If it is non-unionized, you may have some room to negotiate. Remember that compensation includes, but is not limited to, salary and benefits. You must know what you want and what you are prepared to accept. You may be able to negotiate some of your wants, particularly if there is strong interest in hiring you. Be aware that the employer may be more willing to negotiate benefits than salary at this time. Benefits such as education days, funding for conferences, vacation time, or flex time may be more important than a slightly higher salary. Salary may then be re-negotiated at performance review time.

If this is a new area for you, talk to someone who is skilled at negotiating, particularly for compensation packages. Have a couple of scenarios available before discussing your needs with the employer. What is their bottom line and what is yours? If they are not open to negotiating the job expectations or the compensation package, and you are not willing to accept the position, be gracious and let them know why. You should not accept a position that you will regret having taken in a couple of months, but you also should not refuse the offer in such a way as to close the door to further opportunities. Remember, you did have the skills and talents they required.

If you are not offered the job, accept the "rejecting" phone call or letter in a professional way. Bear in mind that not every job will be a good fit for you, whether it has been offered or not. Never burn bridges because another opportunity with this interviewer or organization may come up in the future. Ask for constructive feedback so you can work on improving your interview skills. You may want to send a thank you letter if the feedback you receive has been helpful. Employers may be hesitant to give feedback to individuals who are not the successful candidate, but ask anyway and see what they say. Now it is time to bring closure to the experience and to move on to the next interview. There is a job for everybody; it is just a matter of finding it and successfully promoting yourself at the time of the all-important interview. You may consider it a lot of work to prepare for, participate in, and evaluate your job interview, but think about the time you would spend in the position. You will be more than repaid for the time and effort you invest in the three steps of the interview process.

Interviewing is a powerful self-marketing opportunity in which you can ensure that you have presented your knowledge, skills, and potential in the most positive and appropriate manner. All of the tools identified in Chapter Six and in this chapter are components of a self-marketing strategy. Together they will work to enhance your professional image and give you the edge. Marketing is challenging because, as with other steps in the career planning and development process, it must be integrated into who you are and what you do. It is a valuable part of the ongoing and evolving process of becoming who you want to be and doing what you want to do.

REFERENCES

Trefiak, N., & Volpe, R. (1990). *The interview*. Toronto, Ontario: Canadian Association of Career Educators and Employers.

FURTHER READING

Beatty, R. (1997). *The interview kit*. New York: John Wiley & Sons.

Bloch, D. (1991). *How to have a winning job interview*. Lincolnwood, IL: VGM Career Horizons.

Petras, K., & Petras, R. (1995). *The only job hunting guide you'll ever need*. New York: Simon & Schuster.

Staller, J. (1992). *The high impact interview*. Kitchener, Ontario: Résumés First.

Twombly, D. (1997). *Getting back to work*. Toronto, Ontario: MacMillan Canada.

UNIT III

THE CAREER CONTINUUM

CHAPTER EIGHT

Career Planning and Development for Students: A Beginning

Janice Waddell, RN, MA, PhD (Cand.)

Janice Waddell is an Assistant Professor at the School of Nursing, Ryerson Polytechnic University, Toronto, Ontario, and a doctoral candidate at York University in Toronto. Janice, who has a special interest in working with students in the career planning process, has been an Associate of Donner & Wheeler since 1994.

Nurses propose that client discharge planning should begin at the time of admission to the hospital. This philosophy also holds true for career planning strategies for nursing students; the time to begin developing them is in the first year of your nursing program. New nursing graduates face a broad range of career opportunities and are challenged to position themselves in a job market that is diverse and highly competitive. Miller, Shortridge, Woodside, and Gutjahr (1984) suggest that, with its variety of career options, nursing has a great deal to offer students who are able to articulate their strengths and who have developed a process of establishing their career goals. Students, however, often express concern that in light of the competitive job market, their lack of formal nursing experience will disadvantage them as they pursue jobs related to their career goals. Yet despite the challenges presented by the current health care environment, there is cause for optimism because students can do many things that will greatly enhance their chances of meeting their immediate career goals at graduation. Starting early is the first step. Allen (1997) advises that many of the skills and attributes that employers look for in potential employees take time to develop.

Therefore, if you can start your career planning process in the early stages of your nursing education, you will enter the job market with a definite advantage (Allen, 1997).

Your nursing program can offer you unlimited opportunities to develop the skills and resources to meet career challenges with confidence and enthusiasm. Moreover, the student experience comes with benefits not enjoyed by nurses in the workplace. In your student role, you are exposed to a wide range of clinical settings, you are up-to-date on both theoretical and technological advances, and you have a growing sense of the current issues in the field of nursing and in the health care system as a whole. You are already ahead of the game! Equipped with some career planning strategies, you can learn to create meaningful and career enhancing experiences in both the classroom and clinical settings.

In this chapter you will learn how the career planning and development process described in previous chapters can be adapted to meet the particular career planning needs of nursing students so that they can appropriately begin what should be a career-long concern. Variants of the environmental scan, self-assessment, and reality check steps as well as the self-marketing tips will help nursing students to meet the unique challenges and advantages inherent in their position. To show other students what this process looks like "in action," nursing students who have been actively planning their careers over the course of their program tell their career planning stories and offer suggestions to others ready to begin theirs. Although the focus in this chapter is on students who are not yet registered nurses, registered nurse students may also find aspects of the chapter helpful.

WHERE DO I START?

The career planning process involves thought, insight, and dedicated time. Although many resources are available for you to use in planning your career, the one most important to your career development is you! Incorporating the career planning process as a part of your approach to your nursing education will help you to develop the knowledge and resources to be able to shape your student experience. Once you have accepted the challenge of career planning, you will be ready to take the first step in the career planning process.

Scanning the Environment

Scanning the environment is something you have already been introduced to as a nursing student. As you learn to plan and deliver nursing care, you also learn to observe your client's environment and the broad range of social, economic, and other variables that influence the client's health status. Meanwhile you also learn about the current trends and issues in nursing, in health care, in work design, and in society at large. The process by which you have gained this knowledge is one that must become part of your ongoing development as a professional. You need to learn to make scanning a continuous and ongoing activity so that you can use the information you gain to plan care and to develop your career.

Nursing program goals and outcomes can also provide you with a professional frame of reference to help you focus on broad areas of career development. Broad program goals related to competency in the areas of communication, leadership, knowledge, and professional practice reflect priority requirements for nursing practice and can serve as an excellent guide for your career development activities. Other resources that can provide assistance in determining strengths important to enhance or areas in which to focus your development are nursing journals and career advertisements in journals and newspapers. Discussions about current trends in nursing practice and descriptions of skills outlined in job advertisements can offer valuable cues about which nursing skills are considered necessary in the current market. Chapter Two offers other suggestions concerning how to scan your environment and provides you with a practical and up-to-date scan of today's health care environment.

Your Self-Assessment

To develop your career in a way that reflects your values and beliefs, you must have a high degree of self-knowledge (Barner, 1994; Donner & Wheeler, 1993). The self-assessment process assists individuals to reflect on both personal and professional attributes and accomplishments and to look at needs for ongoing professional development. As a student nurse, you too should be aware of your values, skills, strengths, and the areas that you would like to develop further. Such an awareness comes from exploring the reasons you chose nursing as your career and from reflecting on your professional experiences in academic and clinical areas. The insight you gain from your scanning and self-assessment will form the foundation for all your career planning activities. You should begin developing it in the first year of your nursing program.

In many ways students have an advantage in this step of the career planning and development process. Most nursing curricula require that you participate in some form of self-reflection. Often students submit a journal of their reflections about their clinical experiences, which includes the application of relevant theory to enhance their understanding of their experiences. This reflective process offers you the opportunity to become more self-aware by helping you to clarify your values, affirm your strengths, and identify your learning needs in the context of specific clinical experiences. Your increased self-knowledge can help you to broaden your perspective and to see alternatives for your nursing practice (Lauterbach & Becker, 1996). Taking advantage of the support you have for self-reflection in your nursing education will help you to master the process of self-assessment and make it an integral aspect of your career development and your practice.

Chapter Three provides an excellent guide to help you with the self-assessment process. The questions RNs are urged to ask themselves are also appropriate for you to use to structure your approach to your self-assessment. General categories from that chapter will be discussed with suggestions about how student nurses may adapt questions to their situations.

Values and beliefs

When you examine how your values and beliefs relate to nursing, it would be helpful for you, as a student, to reflect on why you chose nursing as a career. Ask yourself the following questions (Anderson, 1992; Miller et al., 1984):

1. Were there significant experiences, interests, or skills that prompted you to consider nursing as a career?
2. Was there a nurse who you felt that you would like to emulate? If so, what qualities did the nurse possess? What values did the nurse convey?
3. What was it about nursing that made you feel that it was a good fit in terms of furthering your interests and skills?

4.   What values do you hold that you believe are important for nursing?
5.   How will your values influence your learning and your professional development as a nurse?
6.   How do you feel that you can contribute to nursing?

Maria, for instance, recognized the strong influence her mother had on her choice of nursing as a career. Her mother, who had been a nurse, exemplified the qualities of warmth, caring, and strength that the student associated with nursing. Although her mother had not practised nursing for many years, the manner in which she related to her family, friends, acquaintances, and anyone in need demonstrated to Maria her mother's respect for the uniqueness and integrity of each individual. Maria also had the opportunity to accompany her mother when she volunteered at a senior citizen's home. During these visits Maria observed the positive effect both her mother and other nurses had on the residents through their professional presence and individualized approach to care. Exposure to this setting over a long period of time fostered Maria's interest in a career in nursing with a possible focus on working with the elderly. She had also been told by teachers, family members, and friends that she was very good with people and would make a great nurse. Knowing that she had the potential to be a warm, caring, and committed professional, and that she was interested in working closely with people helped Maria to decide that nursing was a good career choice. "It's funny, I always knew I wanted to be a nurse, but it wasn't until I sat down and really thought about *why* I wanted to be a nurse that I realized what an excellent role model my Mom has been and how that modelling has influenced my decision to go into nursing. I also can see how I have come to value many of the things my Mom does, and how these values will help me to be an effective nurse."

As you continue your nursing education, you will need to review your values and interests, adding to them and refining them in response to your growing nursing and personal experiences. It is exciting to watch how your values help you interpret your learning experiences, and how your learning experiences influence your values. Such self-reflective strategies as journal entries can help you to keep track of your evolving values, goals, and interests. You may also take advantage of the experiences of different faculty members. Asking faculty to share significant events that helped them to clarify their professional values and beliefs can be informative and compelling (Miller et al., 1984). Reflecting on her psychiatric nursing experience, Maria found that her commitment to respect the integrity of the individual was a strength in working with the mentally ill client. She used her journals and meetings with her faculty advisor as means to explore the idea of applying and enhancing her skills in the area of psychogeriatrics. Her faculty advisor was also able to identify other faculty members willing to share expertise and resources related to this area of practice.

Identification of strengths and areas for further development

Reviewing past accomplishments and nursing program goals are two means of identifying your strengths and the areas you would like to develop further. As you accumulate classroom and clinical experiences, you will also gather feedback relating to your strengths, your progress, and areas to develop from a variety of instructors, peers, and clinical contacts. It is important to reflect on these strengths as well as the areas you would like to develop further so that you can both structure and interpret your learning experiences in a way that is relevant and meaningful to you.

If you are in the first year of your basic nursing program, you can start by considering your past accomplishments. Many of the successes and strengths you have enjoyed in other areas of your life will hold you in good stead in your nursing career. Review your past accomplishments with a focus on the skills and strengths that you developed as a result of your efforts. For example, Stephanie identified her involvement on the high school rowing team as an accomplishment. When she focused on the skills she had developed as a result of this experience, she identified strengths in teamwork, an ability to balance academics and extracurricular activities successfully, and effective coaching skills with new team members. Each of these skills will be an asset to her in her nursing career. Pushpa was employed as a nanny for three young children during the summer months. She was able to identify her knowledge related to the developmental issues and needs of both the preschool and school-aged child, the enjoyment she experienced when working with children, and her strengths in the areas of organization, patience, and perseverance. Having identified these strengths and skills, students can then focus on enhancing them in the context of their nursing experience by asking for specific feedback and seeking experiences to meet their unique learning needs.

Using your self-assessment in your clinical placements

The more you learn and reflect on your development as a nurse, the more you can begin to influence and direct your learning experiences. For example, if your self-assessment helps you to recognize that you value the continuity of working with clients over a long period of time, and you are developing strengths in communicating with clients who require long-term care, a clinical placement in a short-stay surgical unit may not be the best choice for you. What you learned from your self-assessment can help you to take the initiative to seek out clinical experiences that are congruent with your values, beliefs, and developing skills. When you select a placement setting which is in keeping with your strengths, you can be more focused on both enhancing those strengths and on developing complementary attributes. Alternatively, if you are in a placement which is not of your choosing, you can use your self-knowledge to help you to focus on aspects of the placement that can further your goals, and to expand your focus to include aspects of the clinical setting. As one student found:

> I was really disappointed when I didn't get the intensive care unit (ICU) clinical placement that I had requested. However, I found that on the general medical floor where I was assigned, I was able to continue to work on the skills that I had hoped to develop in the ICU, for example, organizing and priority setting, without the stress that I know I would have experienced in an intensive care setting. I was also able to take the time to learn other skills, for example, adapting care to meet the needs of patients from diverse cultures, that I would not have been able to focus on had I been in the ICU. I still want the ICU experience, but I had unexpected and exciting experiences where I was, and was able to develop new skills through these experiences.

A 4th-year nursing student, Stuart, described how information from the self-assessment process helped him to evaluate different clinical experiences:

> Throughout my 4 years I would imagine "putting on the hat" of a specialty of nursing that had caught my attention for a while. I would gather information about this particular area through reading, talking to nurses, and attending conferences. What I

was doing was assessing the match between my interests and talents (gathered through the self-assessment) and the nursing specialty that interested me at that time.

Through ongoing self-assessment, Stuart had recognized his strength in interpersonal communication, specifically in the establishment of therapeutic, goal-directed relationships with individual clients. He also valued the mutuality of the nurse-client relationship. This self-knowledge helped him to evaluate the "fit" between an area of nursing practice and a unique professional skill:

> For example, I became interested in nursing informatics. I went to conferences, read books, and talked to some nurses in the informatics area. I imagined the work I would be doing and explored what I would need to get involved. In the end, it didn't feel right to me. I liked computers and had a good idea of their potential in the nursing profession, but I wanted to work more with people and ideas, not with machines, data, and policy. My interest in informatics as a focus of my career faded and was replaced by a new interest, a new "hat" that was more congruent with my values and strengths.

Some students enter nursing programs with a definite idea about the area of nursing in which they wish to practise. The self-assessment process provides these students with an opportunity to keep track of target skills that they need to develop in order to achieve proficiency in their chosen specialty. In the initial years of most nursing education programs, students are required to complete their clinical placements in organizations that provide experiences in keeping with the general goals of the curriculum. In these settings, students with a definite career goal can still maintain a focus on developing those general practice skills that will be necessary in their future practice specialty. Clinical experiences in diverse settings can also help students to delineate which nursing practice skills are necessary, regardless of the clinical setting, and which skills are particular to their chosen specialty. As one student nurse explained:

> Knowing that I wanted to focus my career in maternity nursing, I tried to arrange for my clinical placements to be in this

area. When I was in other settings, I tried to focus on my communication and assessment skills. I also spoke to each of my clinical instructors about my career goals. They then supported me to seek experiences in non-maternity settings that would contribute to my skill development in obstetrical nursing. Each placement was a building block of knowledge for the rest…people are willing to help you when they can see that you are focused and are willing to work hard to achieve your goal.

Of course, many students entering nursing do not have a specific career goal. It is not unusual for them to be uncertain of what experiences would be most beneficial to their professional development. However, if they devote the time and effort to reaffirm, discover, or expand their values, strengths, and interests after each clinical experience and academic term, they will be better able to plan for future experiences and to identify their specific areas of interest and aptitude. At the very least, reflecting on experiences and related professional growth offers students information to take to a faculty member or peer for help in clarifying opportunities for further skill development. One student found that by keeping her values at the centre of her planning for her clinical placements, she was able to develop skills and expertise that would be an asset in any setting:

My mother had to spend a fair amount of time in the hospital, and I was so appreciative of the nurses who took the time to talk to us and to help us, as her family, to understand what was happening and how we could help her. I don't know what specialty I want to work in, but I do know that I want to practise family-centred care, and I want to know how to communicate not only with patients, but with families. Knowing this, I make a point to have developing my skills in family-centred care and communication as learning goals for each placement. If I let my instructor and the other nurses on the unit know about my interest in these areas, they can assign me patients who will offer me the opportunity to work on these skills. I find it hard to be on units where there is no visiting during the day and little time to talk to patients; I don't think I could work on a unit like that.

The Reality Check

An important aspect of the self-assessment process, the reality check, involves seeking out feedback from others. It can be obtained from faculty members, peers, or any other individual whom you trust to offer you an objective and informed response. The reality check is not intended as a means for others to evaluate your self-assessment, but rather to confirm the information in your self-assessment and to add a different perspective that may help you refine or rethink parts of it. Often individuals find that the reality check provides an opportunity to be informed, or reminded, of strengths and attributes that one does not recognize in oneself. The reality check component of the self-assessment process can serve to strengthen your confidence in communicating your skills and uniqueness to colleagues, potential employers, and other professionals. For example, during the reality check step of a 3rd-year nursing student's self-assessment process, she became aware of a strength she had not previously identified:

> I took my self-assessment to a faculty member whom I really like and respect. She confirmed the strengths that I had identified and, to my surprise, added something that I would never have considered a strength. She said that my sense of humour was excellent and allowed me to establish rapport with clients in a very gentle and non-threatening manner. Now when I care for clients, I am conscious of my use of humour and can see that it is unique and can be therapeutic.

Armed with your regular formal evaluations from instructors, peers, and nursing contacts, your expanding nursing experience, and your initial assessment of your accomplishments as you enter nursing, you have what you need to update your self-assessment on an ongoing basis.

WHAT DO I DO NEXT?

As you develop and refine your skills and interests related to your nursing practice, you can take advantage of, and create, opportunities to investigate various career options. An example of this was given by Stuart, the student who explored the area of nursing informatics. Your overall goal at this point in your career may be to explore what is available for you in nursing and what resources (both human and information) you may need to facilitate this discovery. There are many ways that you can begin to explore nursing careers. The strategic career plan described in Chapter Five provides you with a process and a structure to help you to move forward with your plans for further research related to career options, relevant clinical placement options and related experiences, and the identification of appropriate resources. You do not have to have a specific position in mind for a strategic career plan to work for you. Instead, the goals you choose to focus on can be directly related to areas of development that you have identified in your self-assessment, such as enhancing communication skills in crisis situations, increasing your involvement in your professional organization, or researching educational opportunities related to clinical skill development. What having a strategic career plan does help you to do is to take your ideas and plans and make them action oriented. You may have more than one strategic career plan at any given time. As one student stated:

> In such turbulent times, I feel that I must have several back-up plans on the go at once. I must be ready to shift the career goals or options I am pursuing at the drop of a hat. This flexibility and multiple career options allow me to sleep at night knowing that if I don't get a particular job, I have lots of other possibilities.

Other students attempted to position themselves to be marketable in a number of health care settings:

> After my 2nd year of nursing, I knew that I wanted to work in the area of geriatrics. With all of the changes happening in the hospitals, I wasn't confident that there would be many positions in acute care settings by the time I graduated. So, I planned my 3rd- and 4th-year clinical placements so that I would gain experience in an inpatient setting, a community setting, and an outpatient clinic – all with a focus on geriatrics. I believe that the skills I developed in working in different environments will be an asset to me in my job hunting and in my long-term career development.

> Unlike some of my classmates, I didn't come into nursing with a definite idea of a specialty. When I finally found my niche, pediatric mental health, at the end of my 3rd-year of nursing, I

realized it had to make the best of my consolidation experience if I was to develop some strong marketable skills prior to graduation. I talked a lot with the nurses and manager on the pediatric mental health unit I was on for my 3rd-year placement and learned of some community mental health centres that dealt with disturbed children. The problem was that most of the centres did not have nursing departments, although they did have nurses working with the team. I talked to faculty members with mental health expertise and with the placement coordinator, and I obtained approval to initiate contact with a couple of the centres to see if I could work with a nurse preceptor. One centre agreed to my proposal and also agreed to let me volunteer over the summer so that I could develop some skills before I started a formal placement.

The strategic career plan you adopt to explore nursing practice alternatives can offer the added advantage of providing you with an opportunity to meet a variety of nurses, and for them to meet you. Each professional encounter you have becomes a chance for you to learn about nursing careers, to express your interest, and to market your growing accomplishments!

The Self-Marketing Process

Marketing in the context of career planning simply means that not only must student nurses be clear in their own minds about their strengths and the contributions they can make to professional practice, but they must also be able to communicate that information confidently and effectively to others. This communication can occur in formal interactions with others, in written form, and in informal discussions with professional colleagues. The key to successful marketing is to develop an approach that is congruent with your values and communication style and that is true to your abilities. If that congruency is achieved, you are not "selling yourself"; you are asserting your professional strengths and accomplishments in a way that fits with who you are:

I wanted my 3rd- and 4th-year clinical placements to be focused on maternal-child nursing. The clinical placement coordinator couldn't guarantee me anything, so I decided, with the approval

*of the nursing school, to seek out my own placements. I had vol-
unteered as an assistant to an RN prenatal instructor at my
community hospital. I told the RN of my interest in doing a clinical placement at the hospital, and she offered to speak to the
nurse manager on her unit to see if I could do my clinical there.
I had an interview with the nurse manager, and based on my
volunteer activities, my informed interest in the area, and references from the RN who taught the prenatal class and from my
clinical advisor, I was offered a 3rd-year placement in the post-
partum unit. I made sure that I demonstrated to the staff and
clients that I was professional and that I wanted to learn more.
When people know that you're interested in what they are
doing, they will go out of their way to help you to get certain
experiences. I ended up doing my 4th-year placement in labour
and delivery in the same hospital. I wouldn't have had the
opportunity to have such a comprehensive experience if I had
not known what I wanted and made the effort to seek out a
placement that would meet both my needs and the requirements
of the school.*

Chapters Six and Seven have provided you with valuable information and guidance in terms of broader concepts related to the self-
marketing process. The following discussion will be specifically
focused on how nursing students can establish professional networks,
benefit from mentoring relationships, build a résumé, and prepare for
an interview.

Networking within your school of nursing

Networking can serve many purposes for nursing students. It involves
meeting with a variety of people who share similar interests, who
practice in areas of nursing that are attractive to you, and who can
offer you new ideas, perspectives, and opportunities. Besides being a
valuable way to establish, and maintain, your sense of professional
identity, networking also offers you the opportunity to inform others
of your activities related to your plans and of your hopes for your
future practice. Your networking activities will likely become more
focused as you progress in your education program. Initially, you may
feel unsure about where the most appropriate place would be to start

to network. When you are not ready, or interested, in choosing a specific focus for your nursing career, it may be most beneficial to concentrate your networking activities within your school of nursing and on the contacts that arise as a result of your academic experiences. As you start to develop some questions related to career options and to define your professional interests, you can benefit from networking resources in the broader nursing community. Remember that your ongoing self-assessment will also help you to identify specific interests and areas about which you desire further information or development.

At the outset of your nursing education, it is important to discover who your classmates are and how you can establish a sense of involvement in your school of nursing. Your self-assessment will have helped you to clarify why you are in nursing and what you hope to achieve during your nursing education. Getting to know your student colleagues would help you to meet others with similar goals and interests. It would also offer you the chance to find out about interesting courses, clinical placements, and resources, not to mention the support that you could enjoy through your interactions with others who are experiencing similar challenges and adjustments.

The process of networking with your classmates can be both formal and informal. Joining student groups and committees is one formal means of meeting and working with fellow students. A 4th-year student described the following example:

> I became active with student groups within 2 months of starting nursing school. From there, things just blossomed until I was making connections with students all over Canada through the Canadian Nursing Students Association.

Involvement with the student nurses association allowed this student to meet others both within the student's nursing program and from other nursing schools. The many advantages associated with becoming involved with formal student groups in the academic setting include (a) the opportunity to meet, and work with, a large number of faculty members; (b) support in attending conferences and workshops both provincially and nationally; (c) opportunities to gain experience in working on committees and in public speaking; and (d) the development of overall leadership skills. Whether you choose formal or informal (or both!) means to network with your peers, sharing your goals and your interests allows them to keep you in mind as they participate in their experiences. You, in turn, can do the same for them as you encounter new experiences.

Faculty members represent another opportunity for networking which is "at your fingertips." Each faculty member has recognized expertise in one or more of the areas of clinical practice, research, and education. As you discover the diversity of nursing practice and start to identify your clinical interests and strengths, you have the benefit of any number of faculty resources for information, guidance, and support. The exchange of ideas can be a mutually rewarding experience for you and the faculty member. Students reported the following experiences:

> In my final year, I volunteered to be my class representative for student council and also became a member of my school's nursing honour society steering committee. These opportunities allowed me to learn more about faculty members and to interact differently with them from the way I would if we were discussing a test grade or paper. The faculty offered guidance, resources, and support.

> My medical-surgical rotation in the 2nd year of my program was on a unit that shared staff and space with a dialysis unit. I became very interested in the whole area of dialysis and decided to try to focus on that nursing specialty. One of the faculty members has expertise in renal nursing so I set up a meeting with her to talk about the opportunities for nurses in dialysis, and to plan how I could arrange my clinical placements in the next year. She was great; I learned about so many resources and contacts that I would never have had the time, or the information, to find on my own.

Nurses in every realm of nursing generally enjoy talking about their chosen area of practice and find it reinforcing to see students take an interest in what they do. Faculty members who do not have expertise in the area that interests you, but who are faculty you respect and admire, still can be excellent resources for you. When faculty are aware of students' interests, they can inform them of upcoming events, articles, courses, and opportunities for them to further their professional development. Another benefit of networking with faculty becomes apparent when you require academic references for employment or for admission to subsequent academic programs. Faculty who know you, and have had the opportunity to observe and participate in your professional development, are able to provide you with a reference which can clearly reflect your academic accomplishments and professional strengths. Finally, faculty can help you to determine which may be the most appropriate and helpful networking resources outside of the academic setting.

Networking outside the educational setting

Your professional organization offers a wide variety of forums in which you can network with nurses. Joining the professional organization would provide you with the opportunity to participate in any number of interest groups that focus on different aspects and specialties of nursing practice. Most professional organizations also have a specific interest group for students. Also, general meetings of the organization and meetings of specific interest groups can offer you the chance to attend educational sessions and the opportunity to network with nurses practising in various clinical settings. Depending on how focused you are on a particular career goal, you can gather helpful information about how best to position yourself to take advantage of opportunities that may become available in specific clinical settings. For example, if you are interested in the area of oncology nursing, attending a meeting of your provincial oncology nurses' interest group would allow you to meet practising oncology nurses and hear about current issues and trends relevant to oncology nurses working in a variety of settings. Some questions you may consider asking nurses working in specific areas include (a) What do nurses do in that position?, (b) What further education would be helpful to gain entry into that field of nursing?, (c) Is there a need for nurses in that field?, (d) Are there different ways to gain a position in that field?, and (e) Is there someone specific whom I should meet to discuss my interest in such a position? Talking to a recent graduate who is working in an area of interest to you may help you to identify issues and strategies unique to new graduates.

A 2nd-year student with a career goal of obstetrical nursing found that networking in each of her clinical placements, regardless of the clinical specialty, offered her opportunities that she would not have had if she had not made the effort to share her professional goals and interests:

> During my mental health clinical placement, I met with the charge nurse to learn about some of the programs offered on the psychiatric unit. During our discussion, I told her that my goal was to work in labour and delivery and that I thought that my clinical experience in mental health would really help me with my communication skills. As it turned out, she was a prenatal instructor with a community clinic, and she invited me to attend her classes and help her out. She also told me about a short course at one of the colleges that would prepare me to be a labour support person. I gained so much from working with her, and I am now certified to be a labour support person!

Volunteer work also provides rich networking opportunities. A 3rd-year student arranged her academic schedule so that she had one afternoon and evening a week free of classes. She devoted this period of time to securing a volunteer position at a teaching hospital where she hoped to do her consolidation clinical experience in cardiology. In her volunteer role while feeding patients, she took the opportunity to talk to nurses working on the cardiac unit and was able to learn about changes occurring in the hospital organization, the implications of the changes for the nursing department, and what the cardiac unit was looking for in new nursing employees. She was also able to work on her communication skills with clients experiencing cardiac problems. The knowledge and skill gained from this volunteer experience enhanced this student's chances of securing a clinical placement in her chosen area. Refer to Chapter Six for further ideas and strategies about self-marketing in a volunteer position.

Finding a mentor

A mentor is someone who takes a personal and professional interest in your professional development. A mentor will guide you in that development and will seek out opportunities for you to advance in your nursing career. A mentor is someone you respect, who possesses the professional characteristics to which you aspire. Individuals can have more than one mentor and may have different mentors at various stages in their nursing careers. For nursing students, a mentor may be a faculty member who has taken a special interest in you, has influenced your career decisions, and who helps "open doors" for you:

> One very significant faculty member took the time to assist and get to know me. She identified opportunities for growth and encouraged me to explore them. She provided opportunities for me to be involved both within the school and in the broader nursing community. I learned from her professional presentation, and she seemed to take extra time to help me with my professional development.

You may also encounter nurses in your clinical experiences, your summer employment, and in your other professional involvements who represent role models for you. Join committees or projects in which your role models are involved. By joining in on their professional activities, you can get to know them better, and they can also benefit from getting to know you.

Not everyone has a mentor, nor is it necessary to have a mentor in your career planning process. However, if there is someone you respect and feel that you would like to have as a mentor, ask that person if he or she would be willing to act in that role. It is an honour to be asked to be a mentor, but it is important to recognize that mentoring someone is a responsibility that requires a commitment of time and energy. Respect that commitment by making a formal request of the individual you wish to have as a mentor. One student described her experience with her mentor:

> I really enjoyed the clinical instructor that I had in my medical-surgical placement in the 2nd year of my program. Even in her role as an instructor, she really seemed to make a difference to the patients. She also got along with the staff really well and was involved in a lot of professional activities. I often thought that I would like to be just like her when I got to be a "real" nurse! I never told her that I admired her; I just assumed she would know that. In my 4th year, she was my clinical advisor for my final placement. She was still as active and impressive as I remembered her to be. I decided to tell her that I considered her

to be a great professional role model. I also asked her if she would be my mentor. To my surprise, she said that she would be honoured to act as my mentor and, since that meeting, she has already begun to inform me of activities and people that she thinks would be helpful to my career.

Preparing for clinical placement interviews

Many clinical agencies now require that students participate in an interview prior to being considered for a clinical placement. You should plan for these interviews as thoughtfully and thoroughly as you would for a job interview.

If your self-assessment and strategic career plan are up-to-date and you have done your preparation, your chances of enjoying a successful interview are high. Clear learning goals, based on your self-assessment and your nursing program objectives and customized to the clinical setting, will be important to have at the time of the interview. For example, in preparation for an interview at a clinical placement agency, one student obtained (a) copies of the philosophy of the unit to which she was applying as well as of the nursing department, (b) a copy of the hospital's strategic plan and an RN job description for her clinical area, and (c) a schedule of selected professional development opportunities she could take advantage of as a student in the clinical placement setting. Finally, she met with her mentor (a faculty member with expertise in her chosen clinical area) to discuss how the skills and accomplishments identified in her self-assessment and her related learning goals fit with available learning opportunities and the philosophies and plans of the clinical unit and organization. The student also participated in a mock interview with her mentor before her clinical interview.

The interview process also represents an opportunity for you to market your strengths and accomplishments. If it can be assumed that you have chosen this clinical placement based on your interests, your career development needs, and possibly your chosen career option, then it is important to recognize that the interview process is a significant step in your self-marketing process, another way to present yourself and market your skills and accomplishments. For a comprehensive guide to preparing for, and participating in, an interview and for help preparing for your first job interview, that is, the one you will get right after you graduate, refer to Chapter Seven.

The Résumé: Your Written Self-Marketing Strategy

Your résumé is one of your most valuable written self-marketing strategies. It is a summary of your skills and accomplishments. A résumé can also serve as a means of monitoring your progress in building the strengths and expertise that you have identified in your self-assessment. Cross-referencing your self-assessment and your résumé on an ongoing basis will ensure that you are keeping current in your efforts to develop in your career. Refer to Chapter Six for a comprehensive review of the format and content of a professional résumé and its accompanying covering letter. With the exceptions noted in the following discussion, students can use the information in that chapter as a guide to designing their résumé. Three unique aspects of a student résumé will also be presented: the clinical experience summary, the list of selected clinical placements and outcome skills and accomplishments, and the documentation of past working experiences, including summer employment. You will be shown how to highlight those accomplishments and skills that are relevant to your nursing career (See Figure 8-1 for an example of a student résumé).

Your career objective, education, and clinical experiences

In Chapter Six, it is suggested that you include a career objective in your résumé. This provides the potential employer with a quick overview of the reason the candidate is seeking the position. It is important to be concise here, and ensure that the language used is congruent with the position available.

Providing a list of selected clinical agencies where you have completed clinical experiences relevant to the particular job you are seeking offers the potential employer a sense of how you have chosen and used clinical experiences to facilitate your progress toward your career goals. List the agencies in chronological order, with the most recent placement first. Under each agency, provide a brief summary including your unique accomplishments and the major skills you mastered during your learning experience in that setting. This short summary illustrates your level of clinical skill development across a variety of settings related to the job you are seeking. Remember to keep it short; too much detail makes it difficult for the reader to identify key points. Here is an example of a summary used by a student applying to an adult oncology unit:

Fourth Year: St. Elsewhere General Hospital, Toronto, Ontario.
Administration of chemotherapy, maintenance of central venous lines, nutritional teaching and counselling for clients and families, initiated and co-facilitated a support group for families of dying clients.

Documentation of past work experiences

Students who have not had previous RN work experience often find it difficult to present non-nursing work experience in a way that identifies skills relevant to nursing. The key is to highlight those aspects of your work experiences that illustrate skills and accomplishments important to effective nursing practice. Some examples include (a) leadership skills; (b) communication skills; (c) organizational skills; and (d) the ability to work independently, work well within a team, adapt to change, problem solve, and identify learning needs and resources to meet those needs. The examples that follow illustrate how two students presented very relevant skills from non-nursing work experiences.

Example 1

April 1995-   Kitchen and Cleaning Manager
August 1995   Bird's View Retirement Centre

Required to work independently, providing supervision and training to other kitchen and cleaning staff. Responsible for planning and preparation of well-balanced meals, and service delivery. Utilized effective staff management skills, including conflict resolution.

Accomplishments:
Developed an orientation program for new employees. Developed and taught a first-aid course for kitchen and cleaning staff.

Figure 8-1: Sample Résumé

Aisling Donovan
123 Four Street
City, Province Z1X 2A8
Tel: H: (123) 456-7891
W: (123) 345-6789
Fax Number
E-mail Address

Career Objective: To secure an entry level position as a registered nurse in the maternal-child area in which I can further develop my clinical skills and continue to grow in my professional role.

EDUCATION

1993-Present   Name of University
                        Baccalaureate in Nursing
                        City, Province
                        Anticipated Date of Completion: May, 1997

HONOURS

1995-1997   Dean's List

SELECTED CLINICAL EXPERIENCES

Nursing Student
- 4th year – Maternity Hospital Labour and Delivery and Post-Partum. Comprehensive family-centred care to women and families. Preceptor for final-year diploma students. Completed research project on alternative therapies for women in labour.

Skills:
Fetal monitoring, vaginal exams, labour support, teaching and coaching breastfeeding, newborn assessment.

- 3rd year – Community Clinic for pregnant women and/or women parenting a young child, who are abusing substances. Acute care maternity unit.

Skills:
Teaching related to prenatal care, breastfeeding, parenting, infant care, and effects of substance abuse on pregnancy.

PROFESSIONAL ACTIVITIES

1996, 1997
• Associate and Official Delegate of the Canadian Nursing Students Association.

1993-1996
• Yearly representative at Nursing Student Council.

PROFESSIONAL MEMBERSHIPS

• Registered Nurses Association of Province. Student Member – Child Birth Nurses Interest Group.

EMPLOYMENT HISTORY

1993-1996
Health Care Aide – Summer Employment
Child Care Clinic, City, Province

• In collaboration with multidisciplinary team, assisted families with well and sick infant and toddler care. Direct caregiver with four families.

Accomplishments:
Provided staff in-services focused on current developmental theories and pediatric pain management.

1991-1993
Nursing Assistant – Summer Employment
Long-Term Care Facility, City, Province

• Provided comprehensive care to mentally handicapped clients in a medical centre. Responsible for direct care of five clients.

Accomplishments:
Facilitated the establishment of a family support group for families of resident clients.

VOLUNTEER ACTIVITIES

1994-1997
• Volunteer as St. Elsewhere and Maternity Hospital as a Labour Support person.

Example 2

May 1993-   Kitchen Manager
August 1993   Arctic Circle Camp
                 Way Up North, Main Lodge

Responsible for overall management of food services in a northern Canadian lodge.
Coordinated human and material services with limited resources.
Responsive to rapid changes in conditions and challenges unique to an outpost setting. Utilized organizational and problem-solving skills to manage rapid changes in personnel and resources.

Accomplishments:
Revised the ordering process for food services and assisted in computerizing the revised process.

   Following each clinical placement or academic term, review your résumé to ensure that it is current and reflects your updated self-assessment. The résumé you develop over the course of your nursing education will grow in proportion to your experiences. As you begin to refine your interests and career goals and start to target specific jobs or agencies, you can customize your résumé to fit the requirements of particular employment opportunities. Always keep a file of your general résumé on disk so that you can continue to add to it as you move forward in your career development.

Your References

Refer to Chapter Seven for a general discussion of references. Faculty members, mentors, clinical preceptors, part-time and summer job employers, and contacts from volunteer activities can be appropriate sources for references for students. It is important that you select referees who are familiar with your current level of clinical skill development and recent clinical accomplishments relevant to the practice area to which you are applying. If a referee is not abreast of your recent work, provide him or her with a copy of your résumé and any other information that supports your application for the job (e.g., your self-assessment, strategic career plan, clinical evaluations or completed clinical projects). It is important to ask referees well in advance if they would be willing to provide a positive reference for you. Offer the names of your referees if you feel that, following a job interview, you would like to pursue employment with that organization. Contact your referees each time you give their name as a reference and inform them of the specific requirements of the job you are seeking.

CONCLUSION

You have numerous choices ahead of you. You have the skills to make the most of what is available to you and to create choices that have not been discovered. Career-minded student nurses should emphasize opportunities. Individuals who enjoy rich professional careers are the ones who maintain their curiosity about nursing and the world in general (McBride, 1985). As a 4th-year student advises:

> Often it has been opportunity over the course of my years in nursing school that has prompted changes in my career goals and options. Since opportunity cannot always be planned, all I can do is know myself, my strengths, my interests, and my areas for growth, and be prepared to jump when "opportunity knocks." You must always be a "go-getter." Don't wait for an opportunity to come, go and get it!

However you approach your career development, have fun! "There is a spirit of adventure we should each cling to in orchestrating a career" (McBride, 1995, p.247). Being positive and active in your nursing education and career development will help you to maintain a sense of optimism about yourself and your profession. That optimism will allow you to be open to exciting opportunities. Good luck!

REFERENCES

Allen, C. (1997). The job market for '97 grads. *Journal of Career Planning and Employment, 57*(2), 47-50.

Anderson, L. (1992). Reviving your career dream. *Nursing92, 22*(5), 121-122.

Barner, R. (1994). The new career strategist: Career management for the year 2000 and beyond. *The Futurist, 28*(5), 8-14.

Donner, G., & Wheeler, M. M. (1993). Taking control: Career planning for nurses [Insert]. *The Canadian Nurse, 89*(2).

Lauterbach, S. S., & Becker, P. H. (1996). Caring for self: Becoming a self-reflective nurse. *Holistic Nursing Practice, 10*(2), 57-68.

McBride, A. B. (1985). Orchestrating a career. *Nursing Outlook, 33*, 244-247.

Miller, M., Shortridge, L., Woodside, D., & Gutjahr, C. (1984). Career planning and professional development: A unique course for nursing students. *Nursing Educator, 9*(3), 40-42.

CHAPTER NINE

Getting into the Business of Nursing

Betty Gourlay, RN, MHSc

Betty Gourlay, who established her first independent practice in 1974, has been a clinician, an educator, and an administrator in Ontario and Alberta. Currently, Betty is a Principal of CarePartners, an independent practice that provides ideas and resources for clients making day-to-day adjustments to health and injury problems. She also serves as President of the Canadian Association of Nurses in Independent Practice.

I ndependent nursing is not a new phenomenon. Before the Second World War, almost 60% of all registered nurses in Canada were self-employed, private-duty nurses engaged by families to provide nursing services in their homes. However, in the post-war years, social, economic, and technological changes resulted in a reorganization of nursing practice, whereby most nurses provided services in hospitals as employees of those institutions. Today, the way health care services are provided has changed again, and new opportunities are emerging for nurses. Once again, independent practice is an attractive option for them.

This chapter will provide you with the tools to "take charge" of your professional nursing practice as an entrepreneur. It will describe what independent practice is and show you how to assess if it is the right option for you. Then it will help you identify the steps to take in planning, maintaining, and growing your nursing business. A list of additional resources will be provided to help you further in becoming a successful nurse entrepreneur.

WHAT IS INDEPENDENT PRACTICE?

Independent practice takes many forms. Nurses may provide direct care such as intravenous therapy, health promotion services such as stress reduction, and occupational health services. Some provide education, such as continuing education for employees in health care facilities, or workshops for nurses about independent practice! Others provide consulting services, such as quality monitoring to health care facilities and agencies, or risk management programs for industries.

For the most part, those engaged in independent practice are sole proprietors and offer the services themselves. Some have developed partnerships in order to supplement and complement each other's skills and services. A few have developed companies and have employees who provide the services.

Rewards and Challenges of Independent Practice

In implementing an independent practice, you will be moving away from the known into non-traditional practice settings where you will risk personal, professional, and financial security. But there is also joy in risk-taking and in attempting new challenges. In independent practice you have the capacity to direct and control your own work; you also have the opportunity to link directly with clients and their families – the very hallmarks of the nursing profession. Personally, independent practice may allow greater flexibility for family demands. It places no ceiling on income, and age is not a barrier to success. Independent practitioners have plenty of opportunity to make their own decisions and to act on their own ideas. They get the benefits of tax considerations as a business owner; and they even get to enjoy the sense of adventure that comes with starting something new.

But in order to enjoy the benefits of independent practice, you must learn how to deal with potential barriers to success. Those barriers include limited education, isolation, dealing with competition, and taking a risk. Nursing education has not provided opportunities for students to learn the management and business skills necessary for financial survival. Yet because continued autonomy is dependent on financial survival, a successful independent practice would place a major focus on its business aspects.

In independent practice, the work and the work setting are different from what most other nurses experience. Some find the isolation difficult. New associations must be found and built where independent practitioners can learn and share to help their practices thrive.

Some may view competition as an obstacle. Others may already be implementing your idea or may come into the picture after you get set up. The challenge is to create a business that is better than, or different from, your competitors'. Or perhaps the solution is not to see the competition as a problem, but as presenting an opportunity for a creative collaboration or partnership.

Independent practice is a risky endeavour – personally, professionally, and financially. But if you understand the obstacles, you can develop effective strategies to overcome them. Then you too can enjoy the rewards of a successful independent practice.

HOW TO DETERMINE IF INDEPENDENT PRACTICE IS FOR YOU

In order to determine whether independent practice is the right choice for you, you must see yourself as a person with a solution to a need. Go back to your scan of the environment and your self-assessment and consider whether the skills and accomplishments you identified are congruent with a career as a nurse entrepreneur. Focus on existing or potential problems or needs that relate to your areas of interest and expertise. Entrepreneurial success is dependent on offering a needed service, not just one that you think you want to offer, which will meet your personal needs.

Describe what it is you have to offer. Ask yourself the following questions:

1. Will it be information that you offer?
2. Will "hands-on" nursing care be involved?
3. Will you assess and refer?
4. Who will your clients be? For example, will they be individuals, whole families, groups, or communities?
5. Why would they purchase your services? Perhaps you are the only one who does what you do, or perhaps your prospective clients are not happy with others' services.

6. Who is the competition – in your eyes and the client's eyes – and is the competition successful?
7. What are you attempting to do that is the same, different from, or better than the competition?

Answers to these questions will help you clearly describe the kind of independent practice you could offer. They will also provide a framework for the new learning you will undertake to be successful in that practice.

As you think about what kind of independent practice is for you, you also must evaluate whether independent practice actually is a realistic career option for you. Consider the following additional questions:

1. Can I financially afford to go into independent practice? Do I need the benefits package available in my workplace, or do I need a regular pay cheque to meet my financial obligations? The ups-and-downs of early entrepreneurship may be too risky for now.
2. Do I like to be in charge when I'm working, or would I rather be a team member? In an independent practice you *will* be in charge and will need to take charge to ensure that your business is properly launched and it grows appropriately. If you are a better team player, look for a partnership or group practice.
3. Do I actively seek out continuing education opportunities? You will need to learn about many new things to be successful in your independent practice, for example, how to prospect for clients by marketing and networking, and how to manage your finances effectively.
4. How old am I? How long do I want to pursue this business? Full-time or part-time? Developing a successful independent practice takes a lot of time and effort. If you are near retirement, such a venture may not be cost effective in terms of money or effort. Think, instead, about joining an established independent practice as an associate.
5. Am I a risk taker? Do I know how to manage risk? Can I leave the comfort and security of my job for this new challenge and see it as a positive opportunity, not a problem? Quite early in your independent

practice you may also encounter unanticipated opportunities, for example, a new office arrangement or a partnership. If you are unable to take the risk, the opportunity which would be good for your business may be lost and your potential not fully realized.

6. What is my unique contribution? It is important to be able to clearly articulate the business you are in and the services you offer in order both to attract clients to support your business and to develop your business image in the community. *You* must do it – brochures, business cards, and marketing plans reflect you and your services, but do not take the place of you.

7. Do I stick to things once I start them, or do I seek new challenges before completing the last ones? Entering into independent practice requires that you persevere in order to realize your dream. Being distracted by too many side issues will dilute the focus you require for a successful independent practice.

8. Am I flexible enough to deal with ambiguity and uncertainty, or am I more comfortable with a known way that works? As you develop your business and seek information and guidance, answers may not be readily available. Instead, only more questions may be posed, which can be very frustrating and stall your momentum toward your goal.

9. Are there family demands that I need to consider when allocating the necessary time to develop my business? Small children and elderly parents may place extra demands on your available time to the extent that you may consider postponing your "launch" until more of your time could be directly controlled.

Your success will require creativity and determination mixed with a healthy dose of realism. If you know yourself, you'll be able to be true to yourself and your needs while you are helping others.

After you have revisited your self-assessment, examine your knowledge of the nursing part of the business you're getting into, and consider whether you need to supplement your current knowledge and skills to be most effective. Since you will be offering nursing services, you should examine what you know about the current practice of nursing in your jurisdiction – the legal authority, standards of nursing practice, code of ethics, the structure of your professional association and regulatory body, liability protection, etc. Finally, outline your knowledge about and experience in running a business. Some nurses have previous business experience they can draw on. Be sure to include those managerial skills you have used already in your nursing practice, for example, delegation, time management, priority setting, and organizing.

Having looked at yourself, your nursing preparedness, and your readiness to do business, use your findings to enhance your strengths. Plan to reduce your shortcomings by getting the necessary knowledge and skills for yourself or by engaging in a business arrangement that will provide the needed resources. Now you are ready to get started.

GETTING STARTED: DETERMINING DEMAND, MONEY, LOCATION, AND PROFESSIONAL RESOURCES

If you want to be a successful entrepreneur, you must start by investigating whether there is demand for your services, how much money you will require, where you will locate your business, and what professional resources you will use.

Demand

One of the most important aspects of any business is to secure and retain customers. A successful independent practice needs clients. If there is no market, that is, if there are no clients, there will be no business. Your scan of the environment will help you determine if there is a demand for your services, if there is a ready market, what the size or accessibility of that market would be, and your chance of capturing the available market or identifying a niche you may serve in a larger market. This information can help you to make decisions about positioning yourself and about which strategies to use to communicate with your prospective market.

Market research, which provides a way to understand your customers, is used to identify markets and help establish marketing goals. Although the services of market researchers can be purchased, a lot of readily available, inexpensive market data can be found in government publications, for example, Statistics Canada or civic planning documents, and in the annual reports of health and social agencies, chartered banks, and management programs, or from projects conducted in post-secondary institutions. The local library is an excellent resource for these materials and others.

Money

Three really important questions to consider are: How much money do I need? Will I need to borrow? How will I be reimbursed? If starting a business is risky, financing it is even riskier. Can you get enough money to start your business?

It is very important to your business success to consider your personal financial situation and preferred lifestyle. But shifting from the financial security of employed practice requires some rethinking. You can help anticipate costs to ensure continued security as you develop and maintain your business by calculating the cost of lost employment benefits, such as health insurance, pension plan, unemployment insurance, sickness and accident benefits, car allowance, and workers compensation benefits. Efforts to clear up any personal debts are positive actions that will be perceived favourably by business lenders. Entering into business can also affect your income tax and your pensions, so obtaining professional advice from an accountant is wise.

If you plan to borrow money, a lender must be convinced that your business proposition is sound and profitable and that you have the ability to make it succeed. The financial institution will loan you money only if your business will generate sufficient funds to repay the loan as agreed. If the financial institution refuses to lend the money, don't be disheartened. They may see risks in your proposal that they are not prepared to accept. Such a response could help you to revise your business plan, without compromising your client service, into a more acceptable and successful proposal.

A major consideration, one that is difficult for most neophyte entrepreneurial nurses, is establishing the fee for your services. It must cover the direct costs of doing business plus contribute to your general overhead and profit. You must also consider what competitors charge and what the market will bear.

Location

Depending on the nature of your business, that is, whether clients come to you or you go to them, location can be a significant consideration. If you expect your clients to come to you, you should consider whether the area surrounding your prospective office would be complementary to your business, whether there is potential for your business to grow at that location, whether it is accessible, and whether the costs are reasonable.

Professional Resources

Using professionals saves you time and increases your efficiency. The following service descriptions will help you in evaluating professional services:

1. Lawyer – A lawyer will draw up contracts, advise on leases, mortgages, zoning, deeds, and bylaws regarding your office location. Your lawyer could determine your need for business licenses and advise you with regard to an employer's responsibilities to employees. She or he may also provide legal advice on wills, taxes, and investments, as well as on trademarks, copyrights, and patents. Your professional association may provide legal services as a member benefit.
2. Accountant – Your accountant will provide leadership for your financial affairs. She or he may accompany you in your dealings with banks and other financial lenders. In addition, an accountant could set up your financial record-keeping system, prepare your tax return and GST submissions, and assist in the selection and training of a bookkeeper, should you require one.
3. Insurance Agent – Your insurance agent will help you determine the degree of risk you and your client are assuming, and will offer a variety of vehicles to help you manage the risk. Two very important insurance coverages are professional liability coverage (e.g., Canadian Nurses Protective Society), which insures you against professional malpractice, and disability or accident insurance coverage, which protects you from income loss, because if you are unable to work, there may be no business income. If you will be using a vehicle in your business, some adjustment to your auto insurance may be required. A variety of other business-related insurance policies are available for specific risks or situations. A clear description of your services and the way you work with your clients will help your agent propose the most appropriate coverage for the risks you will assume. If you will be working from your home, your insurance agent should review your current household insurance policies to insure that the coverage is sufficient and appropriate for your added business venture with regard, for example, to furniture, electronic equipment, or cars.

Be prepared to maximize the time you spend with your professional advisors – they can be expensive. You should evaluate each professional on both a personal and a professional level to determine the most functional partnership – one which may last for the remainder of your career.

DEVELOPING A BUSINESS PLAN AND CREATING A BUSINESS IMAGE

Once you've completed your research, assessed your financial needs, and know the resources available, you can begin to make specific plans.

What Kind Of Business Arrangement Is Best?

Exploring which legal structure would be most appropriate for conducting your business will help to ensure a good match of nursing and business for entrepreneurial success. Although some nurse entrepreneurs launch their independent practice by buying an existing business or buying a franchise, most nurse entrepreneurs establish sole proprietorships because they are the simplest form of business arrangement. Other legal structures for businesses include partnerships, limited companies, and cooperatives. (See the appendix at the end of this chapter for descriptions.) The choice of business structure also concerns whether the business must be registered or not. The rule of thumb is that registration is required if the business is being conducted under any name other than yours. For example, CarePartners would be registered, but Betty Gourlay, Nurse Consultant, would not.

A Formal Business Plan

Before you begin to develop your business plan, go back to the discussion of strategic career planning in Chapter Five. It provides a place from which to start your business planning. Having also looked at the factors that affect the success of your business – personal aptitude, enough money, potential clients and competitors, a business structure, and a potential location – you are now ready to develop your business plan. Many prototypes of business plans are in use today, but if this is your first attempt at developing a formal business plan, breaking it down into the following smaller units may help you to divide the task into manageable pieces:

1. Marketing – may include how you will make contact with your market. How will you maintain communication with them?
2. Organization – if you will be more than a sole proprietorship, a description of who will do what.
3. Legal structure – plan to describe the legal structure of your business, to ensure compliance with regulatory demands affecting your business, and to cover personal legal issues such as wills.
4. Insurance – to ensure that you and your client are protected and that unnecessary risks are avoided.
5. Finances – plans for acquiring money, allocating resources, and dealing with personal financial aspects of business.

A formal written document provides a game plan for your future – where you want your business to go and the steps to get there. It involves defining goals, developing action plans, implementing them, monitoring progress towards established deadlines, and making the necessary adjustments in response to internal and external changes. Having a formal plan allows the entrepreneur to manage change more easily, react to situations more quickly, and take advantage of opportunities when they arise.

Putting Your Plan Into Action

Start up costs may include expenses incurred for furniture and fixtures, such as a desk, chair, or filing cabinet; leasehold improvements, such as painting or a new carpet; equipment, such as phone, computer, fax machine, and books; vehicle; security deposits for services and space; legal and accounting fees; any licenses, insurance, opening inventory of supplies; and operating loan costs. You may not require all of these, but you should anticipate some capital outlay to get started.

Once you have begun, your ongoing expenses may include some or all of the following: space rental, telephone answering service or machine, secretarial services, supplies, equipment and maintenance, travel, insurance, consultations, professional conferences, workshops and seminars, memberships in professional and business groups, periodicals and professional journals, lawyer and accountant fees, personal income, car expenses, bad debt allowance, and accounts receivable. It is these expenses of doing business that must be considered when setting the fee you will charge for your services. Most beginners overlook at least one or two items on this list.

What Is A Business Image? How Do You Develop One?

Your business image should be constructed carefully because it has a bearing on your ability to attract and keep clients, that is, on the very viability of your business. Be aware that a positive image is built gradually. However, a negative image develops quickly and is very difficult to reverse.

Some of the components of a business image include (a) your communication in print, for example, advertising, telephone listings, business card, and brochure; (b) your staff, both their appearance and their attitude in dealing with people; your office, including location, furniture, magazines, signage, and parking access; (c) telephone contacts, including attitude and tone of voice; (d) your pricing, whether it is competitive and fits with the business image you are attempting to create; (e) your stationery; (f) your credit policy for account payment; and (g) the actual provision of your service. You may have decided about each of these aspects separately in your business planning, but they all come together to create your business image. They must work together as a whole, presenting one integrated message for your client and for the community – that of a professional nursing service.

INDEPENDENT DOES NOT MEAN ALONE

While only you can determine the business you are in, many resources are available to provide assistance. The business sections of national and local newspapers, as well as business magazines are readily available to help you learn about business and business strategies. You would already have become familiar with many of these when you were scanning the environment. Libraries offer a wide variety of print resources – books, magazines, flyers, pamphlets, newsletters, etc. This chapter ends with a list of suggested further reading, which includes articles by nurses who are beginning to describe their entrepreneurial experiences.

Post-secondary educational facilities and other education providers offer courses on a range of topics, both for credit and for interest. Informal educational opportunities are provided through professional and business groups, such as the local chamber of commerce. The World Wide Web and the Internet can be accessed for ideas and resources, for opportunities to "chat" with others who have similar interests, and to facilitate skill development.

Formal organizations, both in nursing and business, can be sources of support when you are beginning or trying new things. Nurses in independent practice are organized nationally as the Canadian Association of Nurses in Independent Practice. Some provinces have a provincial organization for independent practice. A call to your provincial nursing association will provide you with the information. Some management programs in post-secondary educational institutions will assign students to assist you in developing selected aspects of your business plan. They are closely supervised by experienced faculty but, as students, their fee is much lower than commercial rates.

You have already learned about the importance of having a network in Chapter Six. As a nurse in independent practice, it is critical that you develop a network of people who can provide you with ideas and connections that can help you and your business grow. Getting actively involved in organizations, especially your professional association, as well as in community volunteer work, even political campaigns and fund raising projects, will allow you to meet and work with a wide variety of people. Remember that the ability to communicate effectively and to network are your greatest assets in developing a successful business. Word-of-mouth is often how new clients find you. The more people who know you and know what you do, the more likely yours will be the name they think of when others are seeking nursing services.

TRANSFORMING YOUR VISION

Many nurses dream of using their professional knowledge and skill outside the traditional work environment. This chapter has shown you how nurses can "move out" into independent nursing practice. It has outlined the necessary environmental scanning, the process used to determine whether you are cut out to be an entrepreneur, the risks and benefits of entrepreneurial practice, and the components of a solid business plan that you will need to guide you on your entrepreneurial adventure and to help you begin to transform your career vision into your reality.

FURTHER READING

Barger, S. E. (1991). Entrepreneurial nursing: The right course at the right time. *Nurse Educator, 16*(5), 5-8.

Bondoc, L. (1995). Market research. An essential part of independent practice. *Alberta Association of Registered Nurses Newsletter, 51*(8), 19.

Brown, L. (1993a). Making it on her own. *Nursing BC, 25*(1), 15.

Brown, L. (1993b). Self-employed nursing. *Nursing BC, 25*(1), 10-13.

Calmelat, A. (1993). Tips for starting your own nurse practitioner practice. *Nurse Practitioner, 18*(4), 60-61, 64, 67-68.

Canadian Association of Nurses in Independent Practice (1993). Group fosters innovative nurses. *Registered Nurse, 5*(5), 18.

Canadian Nurses Association (1996). *On your own: The nurse entrepreneur in nursing now* (Issues and Trends in Canadian Nursing No. 1). Ottawa, Ontario: Author.

Cress, C. (1991). Entrepreneurial human service. Can business and caring co-exist? *Caring, 10*(10), 62-63, 67.

Crossman, S. (1990). Entrepreneurial spirits. *Registered Nurse, 2*(4), 9.

Davis, E. A. (1994). Factors influencing the implementation of the CNS role in a private practice. *Clinical Nurse Specialist, 8*(1), 42-47.

Doll, L. (1995). A registered nurse making it on her own. *Alberta Association of Registered Nurses Newsletter, 51*(7), 34.

Fletcher, G. (1991). A success story . . . independent practice. *The Canadian Nurse, 87*(10), 8.

Grant, A. (1993). Nurses in independent practice. *Registered Nurse, 5*(2), 7, 35.

Grant, A. (1994). Going into independent practice. *The Canadian Nurse, 90*(7), 51.

Hamilton, C. L. (1997). *Nurse entrepreneurship: Seizing the challenge.* Mississauga, Ontario: Prenatal and Infant Consulting Services.

Hammond, M., & Gourlay, B. (1993). For sale! Nursing services. *The Canadian Nurse, 89*(7), 15-16.

International Council of Nurses. (1994). *Guidelines on the nurse entrepreneur providing nursing service.* Geneva, Switzerland: Author.

Jackson, E. M., Hibbert, E., & McFayden, D. (1995). Nursing in transition: Is entrepreneurship the answer? *Alberta Association of Registered Nurses Newsletter, 51*(6), 24-25.

Kolatch, A. (1991). Marketing home health care. *Journal of Nursing Administration, 21*(11), 52-56.

Lee, M. (1994). P. K. Scheerle [Interview]. *American Journal of Nursing, 94*(7), 38-40.

MacMillan, K., & Callahan, P. (1993). Workshop helps identify job options: Entrepreneurship identifies new need. *Registered Nurse, 5*(4), 40-41.

Mardiros, M. (1996). Independent practice in the Outback. *The Canadian Nurse, 92*(3), 20-26.

Patterson, S. (1994). Becoming an entrepreneur. *The Canadian Nurse, 90*(2), 53-54.

Profile of a self-employed nurse. (1993). *Nursing BC, 25*(1), 14.

Registered Nurses Association of Ontario. (1996). *Independent nursing practice: Business start-up guide.* Toronto, Ontario: Author.

Schoen, D. C. (1992). Nurses' attitudes toward control over nursing practice. *Nursing Forum, 27*(1), 24-34.

Slauenwhite, C., DeWitt, P., & Grivell, M. (1991). Independent nurse practitioners: Is society ready for us? Should they be? *The Canadian Nurse, 87*(10), 24.

Townsend, E. (1993). Combining motherhood with self-employment: Consulting jobs grow as hospitals downsize. *Registered Nurse, 5*(5), 15.

Vogel, G., & Doleysh, N. (1988). *Entrepreneuring: A nurse's guide to starting a business.* New York: National League for Nursing.

Vonfrolio, L. G. (1993). Nurse entrepreneur: What are you waiting for? *Orthopedic Nursing, 12*(2), 19-22.

Wheeler, M. M. (1993). Analytical strength foresaw opportunity. *Registered Nurse, 5*(5), 13-14.

Woerner, L. (1994). Business risk and the health care entrepreneur. *Holistic Nursing Practice, 8*(2), 22-27.

Wright, R., & Dorsey, B. (1994). Nurses in independent practice: Is society ready? *The Canadian Nurse, 90*(7), 35-37.

Appendix: Major Types of Legal Structures and Relevant Considerations

	Sole Proprietorship	Partnership	Corporation
Complexity	• Easy to form • Easy to sell or terminate • Business disrupted if you become ill or disabled	• Easy to form • Partnership agreement must be rewritten if a partner dies, leaves, retires, or a new partner comes in	• More expensive to form and operate • Government requirements can be time consuming and cumbersome • More difficult to sell or terminate
Taxes	• Business pays none: all income passes to you and you pay personal taxes • Profits taxed as ordinary income, not capital gain	• Business pays none: individual partners pay taxes on business income and are responsible for expenses	• May be higher than sole proprietorship or partnership • Business is taxed • Advantages in pension and profit-sharing plans
Decision Making	• You do it all • You may not have all the knowledge or expertise needed	• Fairly flexible • More resources for decisions	• May be shared • More resources for decisions
Control	• You maintain total control	• Divided among partners	• Divided among board of directors
Profits	• You receive all	• Divided among partners	• Divided among officers, board of directors, and shareholders

	Sole Proprietorship	Partnership	Corporation
Liability	• Unlimited: personal, professional, and employees	• Unlimited: each partner's personal assets can be seized to pay business debts (exception is if there are limited partners)	• Limited to assets of corporation
Finance	• Difficult to obtain venture capital	• Easier to obtain venture capital	• Easier to obtain venture capital

From *Entrepreneuring: A Nurse's Guide to Starting a Business* by G. Vogel and N. Doleysh, 1988, New York: National League for Nursing. Copyright © 1988 by National League for Nursing. Adapted with permission.

CHAPTER TEN

Career Planning for Retirement

Dorothy Wylie, BScN, MA, MSc(HRD)

Dorothy M. Wylie is retired from the nursing profession. She is currently editor of the Canadian Journal of Nursing Administration and does occasional consulting in health care and nursing adminis-tration. She enjoys her retirement and a variety of interests such as continuing education courses, theatre, symphony, ballet, and tra-vel (particularly cruising).

Although your actual retirement may begin on one particular day, you must plan early and continuously well before that day and well after it to ensure that you will enjoy the retire-ment situation that is best for you. The conditions of your retirement are not preordained; you can have plenty of input about your retire-ment outcomes if you plan ahead. Indeed upcoming retirement, another one of the many points of transition in nurses' careers and personal lives, represents a time of myriad choices. But you must be aware of and informed about those choices and then plan early enough to take advantage of them. To make the right choices for your retirement, you must know yourself, your environment, and what your options are. Previous chapters in this book have outlined a model and process for you to use in career planning. Retirement planning extends that process into the later stages of life.

Planning for a secure and worry-free retirement means paying atten-tion to many aspects of life: social, emotional, physical, and financial. Although the future is difficult to predict, the wisest people consider all aspects of retirement when they plan. Moreover, it is especially important to plan ahead because you may not have the control you assumed you would have over exactly when you retire. That scenario you may have always had in your mind about retiring at 60, 65, or even 55 may become somewhat more complicated, particularly in rapidly changing health care climates like our current one. In such times many nurses find themselves unexpectedly laid off or reluctantly opting for an early or premature retirement because of institutional re-engineering or downsizing. Therefore, early planning is imperative so that you will be prepared both mentally and financially for any of these circumstances.

The old adage "know thyself" was never more important as you begin to make your retirement plans. If you have completed the self-assessment phase of the career planning process, you will be well prepared to begin retirement planning. Healthy retirement requires that you develop a self-awareness about your own needs, likes, and dislikes. There may be others to consider besides yourself – your spouse, family, relatives, and friends – but you are the one who will have to live with yourself for the next several years. As life expectancy increases, those years may amount to 20 or 30, or about 1/4 of your life. So remember that no matter how remote your special retirement day may seem to be, it is never too early to begin to plan for it.

RETIREMENT AS A WOMEN'S ISSUE

Since nursing is predominantly a female occupation, gender issues arise in relation to retirement. Men and women, who have been socialized differently in the past, have differing attitudes towards money and work. Thomas Yaccato (1996) found that men work for money and power and that work is a major focus of their lives. Although money and power are also important to women, they may rank these lower in relation to other items such as independence, service to others, liking their work, and peer recognition. Women's roles and attitudes, however, have also changed over the years, and they can no longer be considered a homogeneous group. Now younger women's values often differ from older women's in relation to work, money, and finances. Some of you, for example, may have mothers who have never worked outside the home and have never had their own money or chequebook; for younger women, this seems almost unbelievable. Today's population of nurses is equally diverse, with respect to age groups and values. Furthermore, at one time most women had to choose between marriage and a career. Now that choice is not necessary, and the majority of nurses successfully combine marriage with a career. Influenced by the women's movement, nurses have become increasingly career oriented, and many have returned to further their education to enhance their career options.

The career decisions that women make can have a strong influence on their future financial security. Traditionally women have been low income earners. This was true of nurses as well until quite recently when, with unionization, salaries became more respectable. During their childbearing years, women often move in and out of the workforce and may engage in part-time rather than full-time work. As a result, many women do not have long consecutive years of employment, which affects their pension plan, their ability to contribute to registered retirement savings plans (RRSPs), and their ability to save. Today, women have a longer life expectancy than men and most can expect to outlive their spouse. Yet some married women may feel they will be looked after by their spouse when retirement comes and so do not engage in planning on their own, or may not even have knowledge of their spouse's retirement plans and financial situation. Those with families may be more interested in paying off the mortgage and saving for the education of their children. Consequently, they may put concerns about pension plans and retirement savings "on the back burner." Although many women, and nurses, continue to develop more independence and financial savvy, others may still be guided by traditional values regarding money and finances.

THE RETIREMENT PLANNING PROCESS

Self-Assessment

Just as in the career planning process you learned about earlier in this book, self-assessment is the linchpin to successful retirement planning. In order to determine your priorities and goals to enjoy a healthy and fulfilling retirement lifestyle, you must be aware of your values and needs, whether physical, social, psychological, or financial. Only then can you take control and begin to plan to ensure that your vision of retirement becomes a reality. Of course you ideally should have been engaging in self-assessment throughout your career so that you would have a clear picture of your needs and goals as you moved through each career stage. Then as you looked towards retirement, you would be able to give your self-assessment a special focus on what your needs, choices, and goals would be after your active worklife was over. But just as it can never be too early to begin to plan for retirement, it can never be too late to start!

Although retirement can bring a range of changes anywhere from major to minor in your lifestyle, or in how and where you spend your day, those changes should still reflect your wants, needs, and values. Your self-assessment will make you aware of them so that you can choose the options and means of meeting them to make sure that your retirement will be stimulating and fulfilling. For example, people who treasure a structured life and a degree of certainty about how their day will unfold will plan the activities and circumstances of their retirement differently from those who realize that they prefer the freedom of a more laidback lifestyle. When you conduct your self-assessment, frank discussions with your spouse and/or other relevant persons are also essential to make sure that your retirement plans will be successful.

As you begin your self-assessment regarding retirement, take a broader view of your life and reflect on the following questions:

1. What are my dreams and what is my vision for the future?
2. What events in the past have been meaningful and given me a sense of satisfaction?
3. What do I like or dislike about my life now?
4. What do I have to change?

You may find it relatively easy to detail your likes and dislikes because these are areas you may have been thinking about on a regular basis. Identifying your own needs may be a subtler matter. Needs are inner forces that motivate us into action. Each of us has needs that we meet in a variety of ways – needs for basic survival, safety and security, friendship and affiliation, influence or ego needs, and, according to Maslow (1970), a need for self-actualization (an expression of creativity, artistic or musical talent, or a quest for adventure). For example, many nurses say they went into the profession to help others, thus fulfilling needs for influence and altruism.

By the time you reach adulthood, the pattern of needs that defines the unique "you" has become well established (Scissons, 1987). But assessing those needs is a challenging process that depends on skills developed over years of practice. Moreover, self-assessment for retirement is not a one-time event. As with the self-assessment you have been doing throughout the other stages of your career, it is an ongoing process that will help you accommodate any changes in your needs, interests, and capabilities that may happen after your retirement is underway.

Scissons (1987) recommends a process of reflection on your past experiences to determine your unique retirement needs. Ask yourself which experiences throughout your career and personal life gave you a real sense of satisfaction or dissatisfaction. Re-examine your life and write down 10 to 15 experiences that have been meaningful to you. Some examples may include your graduation from nursing school, enjoying a satisfying marriage, or the birth of your first child. Others may be related to career changes, such as becoming a nurse manager or nurse practitioner or finally graduating from a post-basic baccalaureate program that took several years to complete. Expand on each situation as you write it out, and analyze how and why it was significant for you. Start to list the needs you identify and the number of times they occur; a pattern will begin to emerge. For instance, your profile may indicate high needs for affiliation, security, and religion, or you may find that needs regarding freedom, adventure, or intellectual stimulation are uppermost. This activity can be time consuming, as it was as you engaged in self-assessment when planning the other stages of your career. So expect it to take several days, even weeks, to accomplish. But each time you revisit the activity, you will build on what you already know about yourself to identify your unique retirement needs.

Taking Steps To Meet Your Needs

Many of the needs you identified in the self-assessment phase of your retirement planning may be related to those that have been important to you throughout your career. But for a fulfilling retirement, you may often have to take other opportunities to meet them from the ones you seized during your worklife. To be successful, you will have to determine your options for meeting those needs, set a series of goals, and plan steps to reach them, as you did during the rest of your career. For example Maryanne, who was a nurse manager for several years, recognized that she had some strong needs she would have to continue to meet when retired. She had always been highly organized at work and particularly enjoyed orienting new staff or teaching students. At the community centre, the principal of the local school spoke with her about the need for a community program in English as a second language. Maryanne was enthusiastic about the possibilities. She took a course on teaching English as a second language at the local community college and then worked with the principal to establish and organize a program. She now coordinates the program and assists with the teaching. Sandra, however, realized that when working she never had the time to meet all her travel needs. An around-the-world trip after she retired had been a long-time dream, but practical and financial reasons led her to plan for an alternative. Sandra opted to take some university courses on the history and culture of other countries and has budgeted for one trip a year to a country she has never visited before.

As you plan to meet your own retirement needs, you should identify the lifestyle changes and practical issues that you must address to achieve your goals. You may not have to face each of these issues immediately, but some preparatory thinking now will help make it easier to make the necessary changes in the future. Some key questions to ask yourself include, "Where shall I live?" "Will I be able to cope with changes in health status?" and "How will I spend my day?" But perhaps the most important question of all is, "Will I be able to afford to meet my needs and the goals I've set?" Your answer may very well hinge on how early you began to plan financially for your retirement.

Sound financial planning

Early and continuously updated financial planning is vital to give yourself the most flexibility to meet your needs when you first retire and when you respond to changes anytime during your retirement. This crucial aspect of planning involves three stages: early preplanning, nearing retirement, and after retirement. The last one represents not so much a finite stage as an ongoing process.

The early preplanning stage can be relatively simple and consist of ensuring that you participate in your employer's pension plan and contribute monthly or yearly to an RRSP. The latter is important whether you are single or married; since the future is unpredictable, divorce or the death of a spouse could have a devastating financial impact if you are unprepared. But regardless of your marital status, the earlier you start to invest and compound your savings, the better, so that they can grow at the greatest rate.

More extensive planning is required at midlife or when nearing retirement stage. Although you may not be contemplating voluntary retirement for awhile, unforeseen circumstances may prevail, such as involuntary early retirement or layoff, not unusual scenarios in today's workplace. Detailed planning at midlife can prepare you, at least financially, for any of these events.

Townson (1995) maintains that to prevent a drop in your standard of living at retirement, your retirement income should be 75% of your gross pre-retirement income. In Canada, everyone upon retirement receives benefits from the Canada Pension Plan (CPP) and Old Age Security (OAS). The future of these two benefits, however, is somewhat uncertain in the current economic climate and with the increase in the elderly population. Therefore, the importance of having a private pension plan as well as RRSP investments cannot be stressed enough.

Complex financial planning requires an expertise beyond the limits of this chapter; however, other resources are available. Some references for further reading are listed at the end of the chapter. Your district taxation office has brochures on tax planning; a number of computer programs are also available. Many financial institutions offer financial planning assistance, or you may choose to obtain the services of a professional financial planning consultant. For example, the Retirement Counsel of Canada is a national network of financial counsellors who provide individual counselling for specialized needs such as asset management and estate and tax planning. Whatever resource you choose, it is important that you feel comfortable with your advisor and develop a sense of trust.

One of the first exercises you must do (whether you plan on your own or with an advisor) is to complete a net worth statement. A sample is provided (see Figure 10-1). Your net worth is the difference between your total assets (what you own) and your total liabilities (what you owe). You may choose to complete the exercise with your spouse, although some financial planners suggest that women carry this out on their own. Determining your individual resources may be useful should you have to support yourself alone in the future.

Figure 10-1: Net worth Work Sheet[1]

ASSETS (What you own)		LIABILITIES (What you owe)	
Non-Registered Assets			
Savings account	$____	Mortgage balance	$____
Chequing account	$____	Loan balance (car, investments)	$____
Term deposits, guaranteed investment certificates	$____	Unpaid bills (charge accounts, taxes, etc.)	$____
Investments (stocks, mutual funds, bonds)	$____	Other debts	$____
Cash value life insurance	$____	Total Liabilities	$____
Real estate	$____		
Home furnishings	$____		
Automobile	$____		
Other assets	$____		
Sub-Total of All Non-Registered Assets	$____	PERSONAL NET WORTH:	
Registered Assets		Total Assets	$____
RRSPs, RIFs	$____	Less:	
Sub-Total of All Registered Assets	$____	Total Liabilities	$____
TOTAL ASSETS	$____	NET WORTH:	$____

---

1. From *Retirement Income Options: Your Personal Planner,* (1966), Toronto, Ontario: The Royal Bank. Adapted with permission from Denise Curren, Royal Bank Public Relations, Toronto, Ontario.

Your net worth forms the retirement asset base from which you can begin your financial planning. Because the exercise of determining what it is provides you with an opportunity to highlight your liabilities and pinpoint areas where you may want to reduce debt before actually retiring, you should begin this activity well in advance of retiring. Doing so will give you time to pay off your mortgage, credit card debt, or any car financing you owe. Your net worth base, consequently, would be strengthened and your financial future made more secure. Your net worth statement is also necessary for writing your will and for beginning estate planning.

The next step in planning your finances is to compare your current monthly income with your current monthly expenses. Those of you who are more methodical already may have a good handle on what your current monthly income and expenses are. Others may have to monitor the situation for 2-3 months.

After you detail your current monthly income and expenses, the next step is to estimate what your projected monthly income and expenses will be when you retire. Retirement income sources may include your private pension plan, CPP, OAS, other investment income, or part-time employment. Martha, for example, was an experienced neonatal nurse. Even after she retired, she was called back occasionally to fill in due to staff illness or a high volume of activity in the unit. This extra income was a useful supplement to her pension income and provided a source of funds for a few "extras."

Determining what your future monthly expenses will be is a little more difficult than estimating income. You may expect that some expenses, such as travel and clothing, will change depending on what you decide to do. For example, travel or entertainment costs may increase because you have more free time. Alternatively, clothing and transportation expenses may decrease because you are not going into work daily. You need to consider all aspects of your future lifestyle and take care not to underestimate expenses. Figure 10-2 gives an example of the areas to keep in mind when estimating income and expenses.

The last step is to compare your expected income with your estimated expenses to predict whether you will have a surplus or deficit of income. If a deficit seems likely, you should revisit the retirement planning process to determine your priorities with regard to meeting your individual needs and maintaining a satisfactory lifestyle.

Figure 10-2: Monthly Income and Expense Work Sheet[2]

MONTHLY INCOME	Current	Retirement
Salary	$_____	$_____
Employer Pension Plan	$_____	$_____
Canada Pension Plan/Quebec Pension Plan	$_____	$_____
Old Age Security	$_____	$_____
Investment income	$_____	$_____
Other	$_____	$_____
Total Income	$_____	$_____

MONTHLY EXPENSES	Current	Retirement
Housing		
Mortgage/rent	$_____	$_____
Property taxes	$_____	$_____
Maintenance	$_____	$_____
Utilities	$_____	$_____
Insurance	$_____	$_____
Food		
Groceries	$_____	$_____
Dining out	$_____	$_____
Clothing	$_____	$_____
Transportation		
Public transit	$_____	$_____
Car/gas/oil, etc.	$_____	$_____
Insurance/license	$_____	$_____

---

2. From *Retirement Income Options: Your Personal Planner*, (1966), Toronto, Ontario: The Royal Bank. Adapted with permission from Denise Curren, Royal Bank Public Relations, Toronto, Ontario.

Health Care

    Insurance premiums $_____ $_____

    Prescriptions $_____ $_____

Health Care		
Insurance premiums	$_____	$_____
Prescriptions	$_____	$_____
Dental	$_____	$_____
Eye care	$_____	$_____
Other	$_____	$_____
Travel/recreation	$_____	$_____
Life insurance	$_____	$_____
Debt repayments	$_____	$_____
Charitable donations	$_____	$_____
Savings	$_____	$_____
Income tax	$_____	$_____
Other	$_____	$_____
Total Expenses	$_____	$_____
TOTAL INCOME	$_____	$_____
LESS TOTAL EXPENSES	$_____	$_____
SURPLUS (INCOME GAP)	$_____	$_____

Although these mathematical exercises are time consuming, they are crucial to give you the realistic picture you need of your finances so that you can take action early enough to ensure that your resources will support your lifestyle choices when you retire.

After retirement, the third and final stage of financial planning actually represents the ongoing monitoring that will be necessary for you to keep abreast of the balance between your resources and needs throughout your retirement. As you periodically reassess your physical, emotional, and social needs, the changes you make to accommodate them may require you to re-evaluate your finances as well. For example, if your physical or emotional condition warrants a move to a retirement or nursing home, you may have to plan to adjust your finances to cover the costs over an extended period. Furthermore, Canadian tax law requires that when you reach the age of 69, you must withdraw your funds from your RRSPs and convert them either to registered retirement income funds (RRIFs) or to an annuity to reduce your tax burden. Forethought about this financial aspect of retirement, and perhaps some professional assistance, will help you make the best decision for your sound financial health. Once you have a clearer picture of what your finances will be like after you retire, you can begin to explore answers to the other key questions about lifestyle choices and practical issues that you will have to decide on as you plan for your retirement.

Where shall I live?

Will you want to live in your current accommodations when you retire? For some people, their home and neighbourhood contribute greatly to their sense of security and affiliation. Giving up the family home, consequently, is a major decision that requires careful thought. Some retirees, for example, make a quick retreat from the city, only to find that they cannot adjust to their new circumstances. For instance, George and Sally, who were both nurses, decided to retire at 58. Because they both had a desire to travel and live in a warmer climate, they sold their house and moved to Mexico. For a while they enjoyed the climate and change of environment, but then they began to miss their friends, found the pace a little too slow, and regretted their hasty decision. Before making major living changes, consider making experimental shifts on a trial basis. George and Sally, for example, could have spent an extended holiday at their intended destination before they sold their home. Similarly, deciding to move to an apartment or condominium may be the best choice for some; but others may find the accommodations confining or lacking in privacy, or they may miss the easy access to outdoor facilities that they enjoyed in their own homes.

Remember, too, that housing that was satisfactory for you in your 50s and 60s may not continue to be so as you age. Health is an important factor to take into account when you consider what your living arrangements should be at any stage of your retirement. But as you get older, think about whether you can still carry out home maintenance, climb the stairs, or shovel snow as you once did. What other plans can you make to take care of these tasks? Apartment living may look more attractive as these chores become physically impossible. Changes in your financial status, likewise, may have a strong influence on your decisions about where to live. You must, therefore, be prepared to re-evaluate your living arrangements as part of your ongoing retirement planning process.

Will I be able to cope with changes in health status?

As nurses, we see patients with heart disease, arthritis, and diabetes, amongst a multitude of other chronic illnesses, and we recognize their debilitating effects. It is difficult to imagine that you, too, may someday be faced with the same infirmities. Yet you must be aware of how your health status may affect your retirement plans, not only related to housing but also to your daily activities and social relationships. Most important, you must be prepared to review and alter your plans as your health status changes. You can take many steps to ensure that your health will be at its best. For instance, regular health checkups, proper diet, and exercise all contribute to a healthy lifestyle. Alice, for example, never participated in sports or exercise because she was always too tired when she finished her shift. After she retired, though, she joined her community centre and enjoys swimming and squash as well as both her renewed health and the extra energy she has for her new friends. Making sure that you have the necessary health insurance to respond to whatever contingencies may arise is also essential as you plan for changes in health status.

How will I spend my day?

As many of the previous examples have implied, social relationships, activities, and interests are all essential for a healthy lifestyle. Whether married or single, your daily routine will almost certainly change considerably when you retire. If you are married, you may have your spouse's support, but each of you must also consider the other's wishes and needs as you plan for retirement. You may, for instance, have to realign your roles to prevent incursions on each other's territory.

Nurses who have been single all their lives, or those left alone through divorce or death, especially must plan for continued personal relationships and activities to prevent their social isolation. Loneliness can be a serious problem for older persons, particularly when friends and relatives become ill or disabled. Taking realistic steps to plan for these needs will make your days meaningful and satisfying.

The unique needs you identified in your self-assessment may lead you to develop new interests, hobbies, or skills. For example, Jean, who discovered a real interest in the history of nursing, became an active member of the nursing history interest group in her professional association. You can nurture artistic or creative talents through painting, writing, and acting, or you may take a more technological approach and develop your computer skills. Exercise, such as swimming and walking, can provide renewed energy and, if done with a group, social stimulation. Courses at local universities, community colleges, and schools can keep you intellectually stimulated.

If, like Sandra, travel is in your plans, learning about new cultures and languages can also be mentally challenging. Several organizations provide special group rates, very attractive to retirees, for programs that combine education with travel. Elderhostel Canada offers numerous short-term academic programs across Canada and abroad that are usually hosted by an educational institution. The Canadian Association of Retired Persons (CARP) offers a number of travel opportunities, as well as special discounts for various products and services, for people over 50 for a nominal membership fee.

Volunteering is an important activity that will appeal to the retiree who wants to continue to make a difference. You can apply the many skills you developed as a nurse in numerous ways as a volunteer. The spectrum of possibilities is broad, ranging from one-to-one activities with children, the elderly, the handicapped or the emotionally disturbed to a variety of group functions. Local hospitals, long-term care facilities, churches, community centres, and food banks all welcome volunteer assistance. Most cities and towns have a central volunteer bureau that will help you find volunteer work appropriate to your wishes and skills. Administrative or managerial nurses may be interested in volunteer work with the Canadian Executive Service Organization (CESO). This group uses retired executives to provide advice and training to aboriginal communities, developing nations and other parts of central and eastern Europe.

Early Retirement

Ideally, the process of deciding whether early retirement is the special option that is right for you should be the same as the one you would use for regular retirement planning. That is, it should be based on the same kind of self-assessment to determine what your needs and choices would be as if you opted to retire at the more usual age of 60 or 65. Furthermore, it would be a positive decision that you arrived at only after considerable thought and advanced planning. Many people actively embrace this choice for the freedom it gives them to pursue other interests in the later stages of their lives. But as you learned in your scan of the environment, the world of work is changing. Nurses, along with other professionals, no longer enjoy the job security they once did. Although many of them may not have planned to practise as late as age 60 or 65, few expected to be forced to leave much earlier. Yet retirement at 45 or 55 is no longer so unusual for nurses in rapidly changing health care environments such as our current one where many institutions have merged, closed, or restructured.

Unanticipated early retirement can have serious financial and psychological implications. But for those nurses who have been actively planning their careers and who have been planning for retirement all along as well, an unexpected early retirement would be neither shocking nor devastating – mentally or financially. The problem often is not really with the early nature of the retirement but with whether it was expected or not and whether the possibility of it was planned for or not.

For many nurses, a job layoff will lead them directly into an intensive re-immersion in the career planning process outlined earlier in this book. They will especially consult the contingency plans about job loss that they built into their strategic career plans (see Chapter Five's section, *What Will You Do If You Lose Your Job Tomorrow? Do You Have a Plan?*). But others will consider accepting an unexpected offer of early retirement. If you ever face this situation, you must seriously ask yourself whether you really are ready to take that step in light of your age, capabilities, and personal circumstances. Now is the time to review and update your self-assessment if you haven't done so lately. You may, for instance, decide that you need to build in a transition period before your full retirement. In this case, you may consider part-time work, even outside of nursing, or consulting or teaching in your area of expertise as means of easing into retirement. The volunteer work you select at this stage of your retirement may especially help you fulfil your needs and gradually put the elements of your new lifestyle in place. For example, Marie, who is 54 years old, and her husband, who is 10 years older, decided they both would retire at the same time. When Marie's hospital offered early retirement packages, she accepted one. But she knew that she would miss the interactions she enjoyed with patients and other nurses and that she would also need some focus outside her home. Marie, therefore, arranged to do volunteer work with palliative care patients for the local health department. Spending time with patients and attending meetings of the palliative care team fulfilled her needs for patient and peer contact and provided inner satisfaction.

ESTATE PLANNING

Like retirement planning, it is never too early to begin estate planning. However, many procrastinate, not wanting to face the implications or the delicate questions often posed in the process. Others may be too busy to recognize it as a priority. The important thing to remember is that if you do not make decisions now, you leave yourself vulnerable to the possibility of others taking over for you, an option that can be hazardous to your spouse and family. Estate planning is similar to the retirement planning process in that you must take stock of your current situation; where it differs is that you must then decide how to disburse your assets to your beneficiaries in an orderly manner. Estate planning includes making a will, identifying executors, determining guardianship if necessary, and defining and assigning power of attorney.

All people should have a will whether or not they have assets in their own name. Your will not only provides for the distribution of your assets, but it also allows you to leave particular possessions to your family and friends. Single individuals should have their funeral wishes and all other matters regarding their estate committed to paper. Standard forms for writing wills are available, but it is wise not to make this a do-it-yourself project because you may not be aware of all the technicalities. It is best to obtain the services of a lawyer or a trust company. If your estate is large or complex, you may want to consult an accountant or tax expert. Remember that an outdated will is as useless as no will at all; so pick a date to conduct a regular review. Wills may need updating if your marital status changes, your assets change, or other events occur, such as the death of a beneficiary or a change in inheritance tax laws.

The executor you choose will be responsible for carrying out the terms of the will and settling the estate according to your wishes. Selecting an executor requires considerable thought. The person must be someone you trust, who is willing to undertake the responsibility and who, preferably, is younger than you. Executors can be professionals, such as lawyers, accountants or officers of a trust company, or they can be a relative or family friend. You can appoint two people as co-executors, which helps lighten the burden. Where young children are in the family, a guardian should also be appointed.

The next step in estate planning is to establish powers of attorney for personal property and personal care. The first grants you the right to name an individual(s) to manage your financial affairs while you are alive, should you become ill or incapacitated. The second power of attorney differs in each province with regard to living wills, advanced health care directives, and personal care documents. Again, as in choosing an executor, you should assign your designated power of attorney carefully to someone you trust.

CONCLUSION

Congratulations on a journey well begun! Now that you have set your retirement planning process in motion, you can look forward to your future with happy anticipation, not with a vague sense of unease. Of course your planning for retirement, as for the rest of the stages of your career, is not a one-time event. Throughout our lives we grow and change as individuals as our situations evolve. Since your retirement very well may extend for 20 or 30 years, your needs, preferences, and capabilities likely will change too. As your physical, mental, and social conditions as well as your relationships change, you will have to reassess your retirement plans. But the assessment skills and knowledge of yourself that you developed through the career planning and retirement planning processes will help you to adjust to new circumstances. Retirement represents not only a period of leisure away from the pressures of work, but also an extended period of time to explore a variety of opportunities and interests. Paradoxically, when you are retired, you can no longer say you don't have the time; yet you may find that you are busier than ever. So make your choices and have a happy, healthy, and satisfying retirement.

REFERENCES

Maslow, A. H. (1970). *Motivation and Personality* (2nd ed.). New York: Harper & Row.

Scissons, E. H. (1987). *Happily ever after: Making the most of your retirement.* New York: Dembner Books.

Thomas Yaccato, J. (1996). *Balancing Act: A Canadian woman's financial success guide* (Rev. ed.). Scarborough, Ontario: Prentice Hall.

Townson, M. (1995). *Women's financial futures: Mid-life prospects for a secure retirement.* Ottawa, Ontario: Canadian Advisory Council on Status of Women.

FURTHER READING

Arsdale, D., & Newman, P. (1991). *Transitions: A woman's guide to successful retirement.* New York: Harper Collins.

Book, J., Cimoroni, C., & Swayze, S. (1996). *Women in the know: How to build a strategy to achieve financial success.* Toronto, Ontario: Key Porter.

Court-Van Arsdale, D., & Newman, P. (1991). *Transitions: A woman's guide to successful retirement.* New York: Harper Collins.

Godfrey, N. S. (1997). *Making change: A woman's guide to designing her financial future*. New York: Simon & Schuster.

Gray, D. A., Delaney, T., Cunningham, G., Solomon, L., & Dwyer, D. (1993). *Risk-free retirement: The complete Canadian planning guide*. Toronto, Ontario: McGraw-Hill Ryerson.

Martindale, J. A., & Moses, M. J. (1991). *Creating your own future: A woman's guide to retirement planning*. Naperville, IL: Sourcebooks Trade.

Townson, M. (1997). *Independent means: A Canadian woman's guide to pensions and a secure financial future*. Toronto, Ontario: MacMillan Canada.

Wylie, B. J., & Cottier, C. (1996). *The best is yet to come: Enjoying a financially secure retirement*. Toronto, Ontario: Key Porter.

UNIT IV

BEYOND THE
INDIVIDUAL

CHAPTER ELEVEN

The Employer's Role in Career Development

Eleanor Ross, RN, MScN and Mary M. Wheeler, RN, MEd

Eleanor Ross has practised as a staff nurse, educator, researcher, and middle and senior manager. Most recently she has held the positions of Vice-President, Academic and Professional Affairs at Women's College Hospital and Assistant Professor, Faculty of Nursing, University of Toronto. Eleanor has been very active in professional and community organizations. She is a Past President of the Registered Nurses Association of Ontario and of the Canadian Nurses Association and currently serves as a member of the International Council of Nurses (1997-2001).

Work is about relationships: relationships between organizations and clients, between workers and clients, and between employers and employees. Until this chapter, this book has been focused on individual nurses and on how they can take control of their careers and their future. Now it is time to look at the relationships nurses have with their employers and at how employers can facilitate their employees' career development by implementing an organizational career development program. Such programs are not new; they have existed in the private sector for some years. It is only very recently, however, that health care organizations, in particular hospitals and community agencies, have become aware of the value of such programs.

This chapter will be focused on why and how organizations should play a role in nurses' career development. It will provide readers with an understanding of the rationale for, and value of, implementing an organizational career development program, one key strategy for assisting nurses in their career development. A case study will be used to demonstrate how one employer responded to re-engineering and its challenges through such a program. This employer's solution serves as an example of only one way, albeit a most effective one, in which employers can strengthen their relationships with employees to ensure that both parties are growing and developing.

Why Employers Should Get Involved with Career Development

Health care organizations are experiencing their greatest challenges in half a century. As you learned in Chapter Two, these challenges originate from rising costs, new technologies, changing consumer expectations, and government fiscal policies. Organizations have responded to these challenges by restructuring, re-engineering, and downsizing. These organizations now require, among other things, a workforce that understands the challenges and is prepared to meet them. Since nurses are the largest employee group in most health care organizations, their employers have a great deal to gain as well from effective organizational career development programs for them.

Health care is a microcosm of the larger corporate world and, as such, reflects the changes that are occurring there globally. Bridges (1994) observed more particularly that North America is in the midst of "de-jobbing," as a shift occurs from organizational structures built out of jobs to a field of work needing to be done. As health care organizations change, nurses, specifically, no longer practise in the same jobs forever. Even if they remain with the same employers, their roles and responsibilities are different. Schaef (1990) found that organizations, including health care ones, historically promised the good life if employees performed in certain ways. Today, however, nurses cannot continue to look to depend on organizations to fulfil such promises, including those of job security or lifetime employment. Because nursing practice routines and hierarchies have been dismantled as health care has been reorganized, nurses' work and roles have changed significantly.

In these times health care organizations, like other large employers, require flexible employees who are receptive to change and who have acquired the competitive employability skills necessary to find work today and in the future. As employees in health care organizations, nurses require clinical competence, expert knowledge, and the ability to be creative and flexible, all of which result in their being in control of their careers. The role for the employer is to ensure that employees understand that job security is linked to their personal competence, transferable skills, and adaptability. Increasingly, organizational structure will be based on work that needs to get done, and nurses will be valued for their abilities both to contribute to the completion of that work and to take responsibility for their own career development and ongoing learning.

Employers' primary organizational goal now and in the future should be to help their employees become more employable. An organization's ability to develop a career-resilient workforce and to assist its employees to understand the implications of the shift from employment to employability will be crucial to maintaining organizational vitality. With restructuring, re-engineering, and downsizing, employees are faced with a changing work environment and the stark reality that old roles and jobs are being eliminated while new ones are being created. Managing in these times can be a challenge for both the employer and the employee. The employer needs the flexibility to respond quickly to changing internal and external forces with new and better ways of doing work. Employees, including nurses, need to be prepared to explain how their skills make them suitable for a newly created job and to have the confidence to risk applying for a new job. The real winners will be organizations that focus on the human side of change, and that assist their employees in being proactive and taking charge of their careers. As Jeska and Rounds (1996) noted, "with change can come change-induced anxiety" (p.343). Those who fear for their jobs or survive the cuts frequently suffer from depression, stress, and fatigue. They begin to "work scared" (Jeska & Rounds, p. 343), which affects patient care and staff productivity. "Career development resources have helped individuals find meaning and purpose in their work, identify new challenges, understand what they can and cannot control, and how to stay connected despite the changing environment. Research has proven these abilities are all critical skills of employees who thrive through change" (Jeska & Rounds, p.343).

Waterman, Waterman, & Collard (1994) said that attaining this primary goal leads to the development of a self-reliant worker and a career-resilient workforce. They define a career-resilient workforce as a group of employees who not only are dedicated to the idea of continuous learning, but who also stand ready to reinvent themselves to keep pace with change. They take responsibility for their own career management and, last but not least, are committed to the organization's success. Maddi and Kobassa (1984) suggested that such individuals possess hardiness, a characteristic needed in times of stress. Hardiness has three dimensions: (a) having control over what occurs in your life rather than feeling powerless; (b) having a commitment to self, a sense of purpose that prevents you from giving up on yourself; and (c) viewing change as a challenge, knowing where to turn for support and resources, being flexible, and seeing each day as an opportunity.

In this new employer-employee relationship, an exchange takes place: the employer gives the employee the opportunity to develop employability skills in exchange for better productivity and commitment to the organization's purpose. Kaye (1993) pointed out that a workforce must be developed that is capable of and committed to maximizing organizational effectiveness, thereby ensuring the continued health of the organization. This won't happen if nurses are underutilized, underskilled, dissatisfied, or disaffected by organizational purposes. Waterman et al. (1994) found that companies and employees are healthier if employees have multiple skills, if they can move easily across functional boundaries, if they are comfortable switching back and forth between regular duties and special projects, and if they feel comfortable moving on when the right fit within one company can no longer be found. Jeska and Rounds (1996) corroborated these findings in their evaluation of a career development and renewal centre in a health care institution. They reported that providing resources to individuals clarified the employees' directions, and challenged them "to grow and take risks, find hope and make commitments needed to participate in the challenges faced during the re-engineering of health care" (p.345).

What Roles Can Employers Play in Career Development?

All health care organizations need to develop ways to assist nurses to understand that adaptability and self-management are key career competencies for the future. One effective approach is to develop comprehensive organizational career development programs that align employee development planning and organizational strategic planning. These programs are focused on continuous learning and on designing and implementing in-house programs to meet employee and organizational needs. Such strategies as job enrichment, job change, and self-development would be supported. A career development program, however, is quite distinct from an outplacement program. Career development programs provide resources to assist staff in ongoing learning and self-assessment, which allow them to take risks and move within the changing institution rather than leave it. These outcomes differ considerably from those of outplacement services, which are specifically designed to assist employees in leaving an organization and applying for a position elsewhere. Such services generally are offered by an external consultant once the individual has left the organization.

An organizational career development program fosters the relationship between individual career plans and the organization's needs (see Figure 11-1). Employees, managers, and the organization all have necessary and specific roles to play in a career development program. Gutteridge, Leibowitz, and Shore (1993) advise employees to assess themselves and develop career plans compatible with the organizational realities; managers are encouraged to support their employees and help them to understand the organization's needs and requirements; and the organization is responsible for providing the tools, resources, and structures to support the process. Where possible, partnerships should evolve among the three key groups. All three need to identify ways to retain, grow, and channel talent that is essential for organizational survival and growth. Investment in developing people is also an investment in the future of the organization. In health care, such investments contribute to the whole health care system as it rearranges what institution will deliver which programs and services.

Kaye (1993) suggested that a successful program is focused on career development as its mission and uses educational initiatives and human resource policies as strategies to support that mission. If, for example, nurses need to assess themselves and develop career plans, then educational programs should be offered to help them understand how to complete a self-assessment, set career goals, and develop a career plan. Similarly, if managers need to provide a coaching support role, other educational programs should be offered to assist them in developing their skills as career coaches. When organizations are considering launching a new initiative or moving in a new direction, and

Figure 11-1: Career Development Systems —
Linking Organizational Needs with Individual Career Needs[1]

Organizational Needs	*Individual Career Needs*
What are the organization's major strategic issues over the next two to three years?	How do I find career opportunities within the organization that:

	Issues	

- What are the most critical needs and challenges that the organization will face over the next two to three years?

- What critical skills, knowledge, and experience will be needed to meet these challenges?

- Does the organization have the bench strength necessary to meet the critical challenges?

Issues

Are employees developing themselves in a way that links personal effectiveness and satisfaction with the achievement of the organization's strategic objectives?

- Use my strengths

- Address my development needs

- Provide challenge

- Match my interests

- Match my values

- Match my personal style

---

1. Reprinted with permission from T. Gutteridge, Z. Leibowitz, and J. Shore, *Organizational Career Development.* Copyright © 1993. Jossey-Bass Inc., Publisher. All rights reserved.

they need to identify nurses with specific skills, they can acquire the information from a computer-based skills bank inventory. This information would be gleaned from human resource tools, such as performance management and appraisal systems, used by both staff and managers to identify skill strengths and limitations. These are just two examples of educational initiatives and human resource strategies that support the value of recognizing and building upon the human potential in an organization. After formal educational programs, an in-house jobs online home page would give nurses access to information about challenging work opportunities what would utilize their unique skills, assist them in developing new skills, and keep them on a continuous learning curve, which would thereby increase their employability potential and the odds of achieving their career goals.

As Kaye (1993) pointed out, comprehensive organizational career development programs must be carefully planned, totally supported, and integrated to balance both individual and organizational needs. Individual talents are identified, and employees are supported in communicating their career needs and aspirations. Organizations, in turn, respect individuals' unique abilities and encourage their utilization by providing opportunities for individuals to develop their potential.

IMPLEMENTING AN ORGANIZATIONAL CAREER DEVELOPMENT PROGRAM: A CASE STUDY

One acute care teaching hospital in Toronto, Canada, implemented a comprehensive career development program as an integral part of a number of strategic changes undertaken in rapid succession. These changes were part of ongoing reassessments of vision and strategic planning processes that resulted in significant hospital re-engineering and program redesign. Nursing played instrumental roles in all of the changes. The Chief of Nursing Practice, as a member of the senior management team, was in an excellent position to champion the idea of a career development program for nurses.

The project began with a review of the literature which confirmed that key to the development of a career-resilient and self-reliant workforce is an organized program of career planning and assistance. Waterman et al.'s, (1994) definition of a career-resilient worker seemed an appropriate, relevant, and desirable organizational goal to set for nurses. Although the program originally was conceptualized for nurses, it was decided that all employees should be included to maximize resources, because the institution was small (216 beds and approximately 1,000 employees). However, for the purposes of this chapter, we will highlight the nursing aspect.

The program was instituted in the belief that career development assistance would be beneficial to employers and employees whether times were good or bad. In good times when jobs are plentiful, nurses want to take advantage of multiple opportunities and employers want to retain staff. In bad times when jobs are in short supply, nurses position themselves to remain employable and to cope with layoffs, job shortages, and competition. Employers want to help staff deal with uncertain futures. All of these needs demand career planning and development skills. At this institution career planning was considered part of a nurse's professional development, since it was congruent with the many definitions of professional practice that included autonomy, self-direction, and continuous learning. The organization believed that by paying attention to the professional development of nurses, it would prevent the loss of competent professionals in whom there had already been a heavy investment, and that if there were job losses in hard times, the nurses would be well positioned to attain other employment.

Change management workshops and education for staff retraining began with the re-engineering project. A Human Resources Task Group planned to manage the transition by using the hospital's Employee Assistance Program (EAP), change management workshops, and education strategies for retraining staff. Career development workshops and a career resource centre were identified to assist staff further through the transition. The Chief of Nursing Practice, the Director of Human Resources, and the Vice-President of the Re-engineering Project together with external career development consultants, Donner & Wheeler and Associates, collaborated on the planning, design, implementation, and evaluation of an organizational career development program. The collaborative partnership of senior management and the Human Resources Department was a key to the successful implementation of the program. The team members were clear that they wanted to implement a comprehensive career development program, not an outplacement service, which several other health care institutions had initiated. Thus, the purpose of the program was to link organizational strategy and people development so that employees could assess their skills and knowledge to position themselves for the newly created jobs and work situations that resulted from re-engineering. The program incorporated the following three initiatives which were begun in sequence: assessing the career development needs of nursing managers and nursing staff, delivering career planning and development workshops, and designing a Career Resource Centre.

Needs Assessment

Both an external and an internal assessment were done. The external scan began with a literature review of the current thinking about organizational career development programs and with a search for "real life" examples from not only health care, but a variety of organizations. Examples of programs within health care organizations were few and tended to be focused on assisting laid off staff who needed to find a job outside the organization. No health care organization in Ontario could be found that had launched a program to help employees become career resilient in changing workplaces by giving them the skills to contribute to the organization's future success by moving within the organization as it continued to reinvent itself. Most programs that were reviewed were from the private sector, notably banking, and were generally well developed and very comprehensive.

Two significant findings emerged from an internal assessment of learner needs. Employees acknowledged that they needed to pay attention to career development, but that they did not have the skills nor did they know where to begin. Managers agreed that they had a role to play in assisting employees with their career planning and development. But they were also trying to cope with the turbulent work environment and were not sure about their own futures. Furthermore, they felt that education would benefit them both individually and in their roles as managers who were expected to assist staff with their career planning and development needs.

These findings are congruent with Donner, Waddell, and Wheeler's (1996), which indicated that more often than not, nurses did not seek out their nurse manager for career development advice. The role of the nurse manager is very complex. Managers are often referred to as being in the middle, balancing the demands of the organization and the needs of the staff (Donner & Wylie, 1995). In the particularly difficult current health care environment, downsizing and restructuring are occurring in all institutions. These changes threaten the jobs not only of staff, but also managers. This fear of job loss undoubtedly has an effect on managers' ability, enthusiasm, and willingness to assist others with career planning. As well, it is clear that managers do not necessarily possess the skills required to assist staff (Donner & Wylie, 1995). As Jeska and Rounds (1996) found when they reviewed various career development programs, significant attention was focused on managers, who were deemed critical to creating an effective environment for career development. Where unique, innovative models were evident, they were felt to be the result of a progressive nurse's leadership.

Workshops

To launch the program, workshops were provided for management and staff across the organization. The goal of these workshops was to sensitize employees to the new employer/employee relationship, which Noer (1993) identified as one that required individuals to take responsibility for themselves and their careers and to prepare for changing organizations and new definitions of job security. In recognition of the significant role managers can play as career planning and development coaches and their unique learning needs concerning that role, managers were provided with an additional half-day session, entitled "The Manager's Role in Career Planning and Development," along with material designed specifically for them (see the appendix at the end of this chapter).

Career Resource Centre

At the conclusion of the workshops, participants evaluated the sessions and expressed a need for ongoing internal support and resources to continue their learning from the workshops. Employees were beginning to realize that many changes would be or were already happening which necessitated that they take control of their careers. A survey to determine the services they wanted available was reviewed by the external consultant, and a plan was developed to deliver key services on site. In response to the expressed needs of both managers and staff, an on-site Career Resource Centre was opened.

The mission of the Centre, which is still flourishing at the hospital, was to provide employees with a variety of resources to help them understand the organization's vision and strategy and learn how to take ownership for continued employability. They would be offered assistance to assess their skills, explore career possibilities, both inside and outside the organization, and make plans to achieve career goals. The Centre provided employees with the tools they needed to maximize their employability and career prospects. The variety of resources offered included the following: a work space; daily newspapers; access to computers, printers, fax machines, and the Internet; self-directed resource materials; confidential career counselling; career development seminars; and employee development/education programs. All activities supported the advancement of individual careers as well as the organization's goals through self-directed, counsellor-guided, and group-supported activities.

The Centre, conveniently located near the hospital cafeteria, was designed as a user-friendly environment so that employees could acquire the resources they needed with minimal assistance from the on-site secretary. The objective was to make the services as accessible as possible. The Centre was open 5 days a week; after hours employees could access the Centre through security. Many of the resources in the Centre were organized according to the four phases in the career planning and development model that were introduced in the initial workshops and were presented in the first five chapters of this book. Reinforcing the model assisted employees in becoming comfortable with discussing and using the four phases on a routine basis. For example, resources in one section of the Centre were designated under the heading *Scanning The Environment*. Weekly media scans were posted of significant happenings in the external health care environment. Relevant in-house announcements or presentations that related to the future of the organization were made available in both written and video format. Self-assessment was encouraged by making various tools, including the Myers-Briggs Type Indicator, available for individual use.

Once a week a career consultant was on site to provide confidential, career counselling. In support of the principle of accessibility, the consultant offered these services either by phone or face to face, at the Centre or on the units. The career counselling sessions gave employees the opportunity to discuss broader issues, such as career options, or more

specific ones, such as how to update a résumé or brush up on interviewing skills to prepare for either an internal or an external opportunity. All employees who used the career counsellor's services received a
follow-up call within 2 weeks to check on their progress. Overall, the
feedback from those contacted indicated that they appreciated the contact and that it gave them a "wake up call" to continue to work on their
own career plans. According to the evaluations, all employees valued
the confidentiality provided by an external consultant.

The Centre also held a variety of career development sessions, again
both on site or on the units, with topics ranging from "How to do a
Self-Assessment," to "Surfing the Internet for Career Opportunities,"
"Financial Planning," and "How to Use Entrepreneurial Skills Inside
an Organization." These sessions ranged from "Lunch and Learn," to
half-day or one-day workshops, all in response to employee need. In
addition, the career development consultant and the consultant
responsible for diversity issues collaborated to design a career development program that would meet the specific needs of the culturally
diverse workforce. Ultimately the Career Resource Centre became a
broker, assisting employees to find the resources and information they
needed to plan and achieve their career goals.

Communications and evaluation strategies ran concurrently with the
delivery of services. Several communication vehicles were used to keep
staff informed of the Centre's activities, including presentations to
management and the Nursing Advisory Committee, along with a series
of "Career Tips" and updates on the Centre's activities that appeared in
the hospital newsletter. A monthly brochure about what was occurring
at the Centre was developed and distributed in-house. Ongoing open
houses were held to keep staff up-to-date on new resource acquisitions
and services. Services were evaluated by ongoing surveys, which gener-
ated both qualitative and quantitative data. Generally employees
focused their feedback on how their self-confidence was fostered
through their ability to use the resources and achieve their potential.
Over a 2-year period, the employer found that career planning and
development had become a concept employees understood and were
comfortable acting upon. For example, as staff applied and were interviewed for newly created jobs, management witnessed the benefits of an
in-house career development program. Staff submitted up-to-date
résumées and were well prepared for their interviews.

Lessons Learned

Before an organizational career development program is launched, careful planning, design, implementation, and evaluation strategies should be utilized. The following points to remember are the result of our learning from the project reported in the case study. They build on the premise that organizations should develop strategies that teach employees how to engage in their own career planning and development, and that organizations must shift their emphasis from looking after employees to helping employees look after themselves.

1. A career development program is a process that evolves over time; it should not be perceived as a "quick fix," but rather as an integral part of an organization's strategy. Administrative commitment up-front is critical and requires the appointment of an individual champion to lead the initiative and have targeted dollars allocated towards the project. In the case study presented, the Chief of Nursing Practice and the Director of Human Resources championed the need for, and the implementation of, the program. However, this example does not preclude that others in an organization take the lead, such as a Director of Education or of Organizational Development. The key to success is having an administrator with power and influence in the organization who will champion a career development program that is comprehensive and well integrated with other strategies that affect employee development.

2. Career development strategies focused on employee professional development must be available from the time of employment and not offered simply as an outplacement service in response to downsizing demands. Providing an environment and resources that foster ongoing staff development to transform them into career-resilient workers and lifelong learners is beneficial not only to specific organizations, but also to the whole health care system as it revamps where, for whom, and how programs are delivered.

3. The target group must be determined from the beginning. Will the program be organization wide or focused on a particular group, for example, nurses. From our experience in a small teaching hospital, moving to an integrated hospital-wide program was an efficient

way to provide the services. Perhaps a larger institution or organization would find the implementation more manageable if phased in using nursing as the first group, since it usually represents the largest employee group.

4. Coordination of activities to maximize resources is essential. Ways to integrate educational initiatives, human resource strategies, and career development must be articulated at the very beginning of the project.

5. Key people, who must be involved in the planning process, should include not only senior management, but unionized and non-unionized staff. From our process, it is evident that an important first step would be a thorough assessment of organizational and employees' needs and wants.

6. To encourage employees to use the resources of the programs, employers must consider varying learning styles, be mindful of workforce diversity, and provide services that are highly visible and easily accessible. In our case study, the Centre's location in a main hallway near the cafeteria provided easy access and, therefore, employees frequented it. New resources are continually required to enhance the centre's relevance as well as to encourage the staff to use the centre. The newspapers, fax machine, and Internet access were well used. Our Diversity Consultant assisted the team in supporting all staff, including the many professionals, housekeeping, and dietary staff.

7. Employees need to feel that skilled persons are available with whom they can interact and seek guidance. Moreover, staff must trust that confidentiality is maintained. Contracting with outside experts, as we did, to manage the counselling aspect of the Career Resource Centre is one way to keep career development separate from performance management. The external consultant was also used to provide educational offerings. Human Resources and Education Departments, if the organization is large enough to have such services, can provide ongoing educational sessions as well.

8. A comprehensive communications strategy should be developed along with the program. This approach is essential to convey the message that career development is highly valued and encouraged within the organization. The organization's strategic goals, visions, and changes need to be reinforced. Similarly, the role of

the career development services should be continuously clarified and reinforced. The fact that the services were not for outplacement purposes needed to be restated in our case because of the turbulent environment and the high level of uncertainty employees experienced externally as well as internally.

9. With the design of the program, evaluation strategies should be included. The evaluation components can vary from immediate to long term, employee as well as manager and organization satisfaction. Whose needs are being met? A successful program will meet both the needs of the employee and the employer.

CONCLUSION

Organizational career development is a key aspect of managing for the future. It also can be an important vehicle for employers to use to support their employees in becoming career resilient. David Noer (1993), of the Centre for Creative Leadership, predicts that organizations that participate in organizational career development will be on the cutting edge. When employers and employees engage in a career development partnership, both partners win.

REFERENCES

Bridges, W. (1994). *Job Shift*. Reading, MA: Addison-Wesley.

Donner, G., Waddell, J., & Wheeler, M. (1996). *Career planning and development: An evaluation project*. Toronto, Ontario: Provincial Nursing Administrators Interest Group.

Donner, G., & Wylie, D. (1995). *The nurse manager in Ontario hospitals: The crucial link to quality work environments*. Toronto, Ontario: Ontario Ministry of Health, Nursing Innovation Program.

Gutteridge, T., Leibowitz, Z., & Shore, J. (1993). *Organizational career development*. San Francisco: Jossey-Bass.

Jeska, S., & Rounds, R. (1996). Addressing the human side of change: Career development and renewal. *Nursing Economics, 14,* 339-345.

Kaye, B. (1993). *Up is not the only way: A guide to developing workforce talent*. Washington, DC: Career Systems.

Maddi, S., & Kobassa, S. C. (1984). *The hardy executive: Health under stress*. Homewood, IL: Dow-Jones-Irwin.

Noer, D. (1993). *Healing the wounds: Overcoming the trauma of layoffs and revitalizing downsized organizations*. San Francisco: Jossey-Bass.

Schaef, A. (1990). *The addictive organization*. San Francisco: Harper & Row.

Waterman, R. H., Waterman, J. A., & Collard, B. (1994). Toward a career-resilient workforce. *Harvard Business Review, 72*(4), 87-95.

FURTHER READING

Barner, R. (1994). The new career strategist: Career management for the year 2000 and beyond. *The Futurist, 28*(5), 8-14.

Barr, N. J., & Desnoyer, J. M. (1988). Career development for the professional nurse: A working model. *The Journal of Continuing Education in Nursing, 19*(2), 68-72.

Caudron, Shari. (1994, April). HR revamps career itineraries. *Personnel Journal*. pp. 64B-64P.

Foot, D. (1996). *Boom, bust & echo: How to profit from the coming demographic shift*. Toronto, Ontario: Stoddart.

Foord, K. J. (1996). *Survivability: Career strategies for the new world of work*. Kelowna, British Columbia: Kirkfoord Communications.

Hakim, C. (1995). *We are all self-employed*. San Francisco: Barrett-Koehler.

Handy, C. (1989). *The age of unreason*. London: Arrow Books.

Howard, A. (1995). *The changing nature of work*. San Francisco: Jossey-Bass.

Knowdell, R. (1996). *Building a career development program*. Palo Alto, CA: Davies-Black.

Kummerow, J. (1991). *New directions in career planning and the workplace*. Palo Alto, CA: Davies-Black.

London, M. (1995). *Employees, careers, and job creation*. San Francisco: Jossey-Bass.

Senge, Peter. (1990). *The fifth discipline*. New York: Doubleday.

Sovie, M. (1982). Fostering professional nursing careers in hospitals: The role of staff development. *Journal of Nursing Administration, 12*(12), 5-10.

Appendix: The Manager's Role in Career Planning

As a manager, you have a number of opportunities to assist staff with their career planning. Your role as coach, support, and mentor is an important one; it will make the difference in staff satisfaction, productivity, and turnover. It will also help you recruit the "best and the brightest."

Recruitment:
This is where your career developer role begins.
In the initial interview with a prospective employee:
- become familiar with the candidate's goals
- determine whether and how you can help him/her meet those goals
- talk about how your unit/agency fits the candidate's objectives

At Time of Hire:
Work with the employee to develop objectives, short- and long-term:
- make the plan part of the employee record
- the plan should include not only practice objectives related to patient care, but also development objectives, (e.g., committee, professional work) and educational goals

At Regular Performance Appraisal:
- review objectives, paying attention to professional development and educational objectives
- work *together* with the employee to revisit the plan, evaluate progress to date and determine any revisions/subtractions/additions to the plan

Ongoing:
- spend time on a regular basis discussing professional development opportunities
- ensure that staff see you as a resource, or if you feel your skills are limited, as access to a resource
- make sure staffing plans, both daily and long-term, recognize the need for development and allow time for that development
- keep yourself informed as to opportunities in your agency, and in the field generally

Exit Interview:
- when an employee leaves, whether through internal transfer or to go elsewhere, you have an opportunity to review career goals and to obtain feedback on how you have helped the employee's development

CHAPTER TWELVE

Alone and Together: Forging Partnerships in Career Planning

Gail J. Donner, RN, PhD and Mary M. Wheeler, RN, MEd

A career is personal and individual; it is about an individual's values, choices, goals, and plans. But planning and developing our careers are activities that we engage in both alone and in partnership with others, in a quiet and private place as well as in a complex and busy workplace or professional environment. Career planning is an ongoing process that is more like a spiral than a straight line. As we continuously move back and forth in the process, we bring new learnings from each experience to the next. To be successful, career planning and development must become an integral part of our professional development, that is, it must be situated within our lives and careers, and not be something we engage in as an occasional act. Just as we are continuously developing our clinical, administrative, teaching, and research skills, so too must we continue to develop our career building skills.

Waterman, Waterman, & Collard's (1994) definition of career resilience is congruent with the many definitions of nursing professional practice that include autonomy, self-direction, and continuous learning. Career-resilient workers take responsibility for their own career management, keep pace with change, and remain committed to the workplace's goals. Career development embodies all of those qualities and behaviours and must be integrated as part of our quest for self-determination as professionals. This book has been about helping nurses to do that – to learn the why and the how of career planning and also to begin to integrate the associated skills and consciousness into their everyday professional and personal lives.

But, as in life generally, we have many partners who help us grow, develop, and achieve our goals. So it is with career planning and development. Throughout the book, we have identified some of those partners – educators, employers, and colleagues. Those partners and others are vital resources in whom we can rely on our journey along our individual career paths. In this chapter, as a way of bringing the career development process full circle, we will highlight the many partners who can help ensure that our career development is rich and rewarding and that we realize our vision and goals. It is directed not only to the individual nurse, but also to the educators, employers, and professional associations and unions that should be partners in the creation of nursing's future.

Educators

As Janice Waddell demonstrated in Chapter Eight, students can use their educational experience to help reach their longer-term career goals. Schools of nursing have both the opportunity and the responsibility to work with students to help them achieve their educational as well as their career goals. By paying attention to students' values, interests, and goals, educators can help them use their clinical experiences to network, to develop appropriate and marketable skills, and to position themselves for future job and career opportunities. Schools of nursing also have other opportunities to help students integrate career planning into their professional development and to provide them with the skills they will need if they are to become career-resilient professionals.

These skills can be developed in two ways. First, schools of nursing should provide opportunities for students to learn and to use the career planning process. Educators can introduce students to the career planning model presented in this book and give them opportunities to apply the model throughout their educational program as they plan clinical experiences and towards the end of the program as they engage in the job search process. Second and more important, schools of nursing must help students understand how career planning is more than preparation for a job, and how it must become a continuous and automatic part of their ongoing professional development. Both of these goals can be achieved by means of formal class preparation, individual student-faculty meetings, the clinical evaluation process, and the specific "career development days" that are becoming more common in schools of nursing. Collaboration with employers, alumnae, and members of other faculties can further enrich the career development part of the nursing curriculum.

Since continuing education is a fact of professional life, career planning and development topics should be incorporated into continuing education programs. Such programs could provide nurses with the opportunity to complete some or all of the four phases of the career planning process and could provide the occasion for individual career planning consultation and advice. Most important, continuing educators must begin to include career development as a part of their clinical and professional programs.

Employers

In Chapter Eleven, Eleanor Ross and Mary Wheeler introduced the concept of organizational career development and provided you with an example of a comprehensive career development program that was conducted in a hospital setting. The employer's participation in career development is essential not only if nurses are to grow and develop as professionals, but also if the organization is to achieve its goals. The employer's role can be enacted both through workplace policy and by the many individual players and departments within the workplace.

Nurse managers have both a responsibility and an opportunity to assist nurses with career development. But if managers are to fulfil a professional development role, it must be clearly identified, its connection to performance appraisal, promotion, and opportunities for change and growth must be articulated, and the manager must be helped to develop the required coaching and mentoring skills. These stipulations can be met through courses, workshops, and formal education in human resource management. Additionally, however, the managers themselves need support and mentoring. They need superiors who help them take control of their careers, who take an interest in their potential (not just within the organization, but in general), who help them identify their strengths and limitations, and who help them plan their growth and development. In other words, they need senior managers who embody enlightened human resource management, especially in difficult times.

However, it may not be possible for nurse managers to assume this human resource development role in times of great change and stress. If nurse managers cannot provide this support, then the employer must find other ways through its human resources or education department in which to offer career development assistance to its staff. Staff development initiatives represent one potential way for this to occur. Staff development departments are focused on continuous learning and on designing and implementing in-house programs to meet the employee's and the employer's needs. These programs should support the advancement of individual careers as well as the organization's goals, thereby ensuring that both parties grow and develop. In the same way, clinical educators must ensure that orientation programs, clinical skills programs, and general professional education programs are integrated with the performance management and career development programs that the workplace provides. If a competent and confident workforce is the key to organizational success, then leadership in career development is not an option for employers.

Professional Organizations

Professional organizations (professional associations, regulatory bodies, and unions) have traditionally made significant contributions towards their members' career development. Career planning programs, leadership and labour relations workshops and seminars, and ongoing opportunities for participation, leadership and networking have been the hallmarks of those organizations' roles. Professional organizations have also been a major source of mentors and mentoring opportunities for nurses. Whether identified as part of career development or not, these activities and programs have clearly made valuable contributions to both the career planning skills and the career successes of members. This activity must continue to be perceived as a priority for professional organizations and must be formalized as part of the organization's mission, mandate, and goals.

Professional organizations are key resources for us throughout our professional lives, regardless of where we work or what roles we play. It is through professional organizations that the true integration of career planning with professional development can occur. Professional organizations have their members as their primary priority and recognize that, "The professionalism of nursing will be achieved only through the professionhood of its members" (Styles, 1982, p.8). It is this "professionhood" that enables the nurse to provide high quality care and to participate in building a quality health care system.

Who and What Else?

Numerous other resources are available to help us achieve our career goals. Family, friends, and colleagues are part of our ongoing support network and, as we learned earlier in this book, can perform a vital function in the career planning process. While we need time and privacy to reflect on who we are, what we value, and what we want, we need others to help us validate those thoughts and assist us to plan and implement our futures.

Of course, most of us go to books and, increasingly, to computers when we need additional help. Following each chapter in this book are lists of references cited in the chapter and also some additional readings that we have found useful. Examine the holdings in your public library. The Internet is also an increasingly reliable source of career planning and development information and support, so get on-line and discover an amazing array of resources that can help you.

Although most of us will engage in career planning on our own and with friends and colleagues, some of us may feel we need additional professional help. Career counsellors may be required from time to time, either those in independent practice or those who are part of workplace employee assistance programs or associated with local YM/YWCAs, colleges, or universities. If you feel you need that additional help, be sure you use the services of well recommended and well prepared professionals.

Some Final Thoughts

Margaretta Styles (1988) once called nursing "an exquisite obsession" (p.113). For us, nursing provides a unique and genuine opportunity to make a meaningful difference in people's lives. We have written this book because, over the past several years, nurses have been telling us about their nursing lives and about their visions, hopes, and goals. They have described the work they do and the importance it has for them, and they have challenged us to help them find ways to do the best work they can. At this time in our history when change and uncertainty seem to dominate the health care environment, many nurses undoubtedly have been forced to question and debate their own personal futures in nursing and perhaps the future of the profession itself. We believe that career planning and development makes a significant contribution towards enabling nurses to be the most they can be and do the best they can do. We have no doubts about our collective future and hope this book has encouraged you to continue to find your path, to continue to grow and develop, and to continue to make the differences that count to so many people.

REFERENCES

Styles, M. M. (1982). *On nursing: Toward a new endowment.* St. Louis, MO: C.V. Mosby.

Waterman, R. H., Waterman, J. A., & Collard, B. J. (1994). Toward a career-resilient workforce. *Harvard Business Review, 72*(4), 87-95.